Robert L. Boylestad
Gabriel Kousourou

Queensborough Community College

EXPERIMENTS IN CIRCUIT ANALYSIS

to accompany
Introductory Circuit Analysis

4th Edition

Charles E. Merrill Publishing Company
A Bell & Howell Company
Columbus   Toronto   London   Sydney

To our wives and children

Published by Charles E. Merrill Publishing Co.
A Bell & Howell Company
Columbus, Ohio 43216

This book was set in *Times Roman and Lubalin Graph*
Copy editor: *Lori Opre*
Cover design coordination: *Ann Mirels*
Text design and
    production coordination: *Ben Shriver*

International Standard Book Number: 0–675–09858-0
Printed in the United States of America
2 3 4 5 6 7 8 9 10—88 87 86 85 84 83

The primary objective of any laboratory text is to correlate theory and practice. This is especially important for the technical career student, for whom this manual has been specifically written.

These experiments are designed to complement the text *Introductory Circuit Analysis,* 4th ed., by Robert L. Boylestad, published by Charles E. Merrill Publishing Company. They have been developed and tested over the past five years at the authors' school.

The original set of experiments has been updated and improved. The new experiments have been devised to reflect recent additions to the text.

Furthermore, power and equipment requirements have been further reduced to afford a greater degree of adaptability to the existing equipment in most schools.

This laboratory text is readily adaptable to a two-semester course in basic electrical circuit analysis. The first half is devoted to dc circuits, while the second half is concerned with sinusoidal and nonsinusoidal ac circuits.

We are deeply indebted to Professor Joseph B. Aidala, of Queensborough Community College, whose work has formed the basis for many of these experiments, and who gave freely of his advice and time during the preparation of this manuscript. We are also grateful to the other members of the department for their constructive suggestions.

Robert L. Boylestad
Gabriel Kousourou

Preface

dc EXPERIMENTS

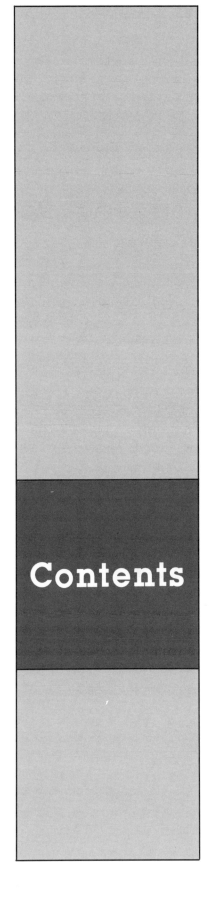

Contents

ac EXPERIMENTS

APPENDICES

Use of the dc Power Supply and dc Meters

Experiment dc

1

OBJECT

To become familiar with the use of the laboratory dc power supply and the various dc meters.

EQUIPMENT REQUIRED

Resistors

1—91 Ω, 220 Ω, 2.2 kΩ, 10 kΩ, 1 MΩ

1—1/2-W, and 1-W carbon (any nominal value)

Instruments

1—dc Power supply 0–30 V, 0–500 mA (minimum)

1—VOM (volt-ohm-milliammeter)

1—DMM (digital multi-meter)

EQUIPMENT ISSUED

TABLE 1.1

Item	Manufacturer and Model No.	Laboratory Serial No.
VOM		
DMM		
Power Supply		

TABLE 1.2

Resistors	
Nominal Value	**Measured Value**
$91\,\Omega$	
$220\,\Omega$	
$2{,}200\,\Omega$	
$10{,}000\,\Omega$	
$1.0\,\mathrm{M}\Omega$	

DESCRIPTION OF APPARATUS

In any active circuit there must be a source of power. In the laboratory, it is convenient to use a source that requires little maintenance and, more important, whose output voltage can easily be varied. Power supplies are rated as to maximum voltage and current output. For example, a supply may be rated 0–40 V at 500 mA, which means that the maximum output voltage at the terminals is 40 V and no more than 500 mA of current should ever be demanded. Extreme care should be exercised so that the maximum current rating is not exceeded. Otherwise the supply may be damaged.

Power supplies in general have three terminals labeled as follows:

The variable output voltage is across the positive and negative terminals. It is often necessary in certain applications that one or the other (positive or negative terminals) be connected to ground. Having the ground brought to the front panel of the supply facilitates these connections [Figs. 1.1(a) and 1.1(b)]. On other occasions it may be required that two or more supplies be connected together for higher output voltages. In this case neither of the two output terminals are grounded [as shown in Fig. 1.1(c)]. The purpose of grounding one of the terminals is for safety. In the event that there is an accident, the current will be conducted to ground rather than through the person operating the equipment.

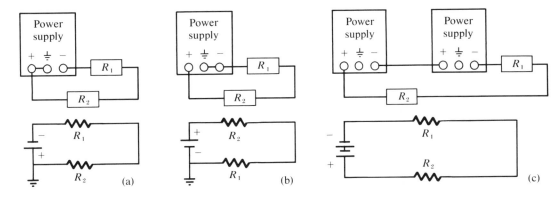

FIG. 1.1

In the experiment you will receive two types of multimeters. These are multipurpose, multirange instruments that can measure a variety of electrical parameters, such as voltage, current, and resistance. One is an analog type; the readout is a conventional movable pointer moving across a scaled meter face. This particular one is called a volt-ohm-milliammeter (VOM). The other is of the digital type; the reading is directly in numerical digits. This type is called a digital multimeter (DMM). As indicated earlier, each will measure resistance, but the VOM requires some special methods, which are covered in Appendix III. Please read this section before using the VOM for resistance measurements.

When using voltmeters, ammeters, or ohmmeters there are several rules that must be observed:

1. Voltmeters are *always* connected in *parallel*.
2. Ammeters are *always* connected in *series*.
3. When using multirange instruments (voltmeters and ammeters), *always* start with the highest range.
4. Ohmmeters are *never* applied to an *energized* circuit.

The accuracy of any measuring instrument is of primary importance. The accuracy of each of the given meters is expressed differently. The VOM accuracy is given as a percentage of the full-scale deflection (FSD), while that of the DMM is slated as a percentage of the reading plus or minus a certain number of digits. You should always be familiar with the accuracies of all of the instruments that you use or your measurements can be quite meaningless.

RÉSUMÉ OF THEORY

Resistors come in various shapes, forms, and materials. The most common types are the carbon and the wirewound.

There are three quantities one must know about a resistor to use it effectively:

1. Resistance value
2. Tolerance
3. Maximum power that the resistor can safely dissipate

A system of color coding has been developed for small resistors to indicate the value and tolerance. The maximum power dissipation is indicated by the physical size of the resistor body. Appendix I shows the various color codes used in resistor marking.

Resistance may be measured either directly with an ohmmeter or indirectly by measuring V and I and calculating R from Ohm's law

$$R = \frac{V}{I}$$ (1.1)

where V is the voltage across the resistor and I is the current through it. For a compatible system of units, R is in ohms, I is in amperes, and V is in volts; of if R is in kilohms, I is in milliamperes, and V is in volts.

PROCEDURE

The purpose of this first experiment is to acquaint you with equipment, so *do not rush*. Learn how to read the meter scales accurately and take your data carefully. Construct your circuits carefully making sure to check the wiring diagram continuously. A good procedure is to have each member of the squad recheck the wiring. If there is any uncertainty, do not hesitate to ask your instructor. When a meter reads down-scale, turn off the power to the circuit immediately and reverse the connections to the meter. When there is more than one scale on a meter, make sure you are reading the correct scale by having other squad members check your reading. If there is a discrepancy, consult the instructor.

Part 1

(a) In the space below, draw the physical size of a 1/2-W, 1-W, and 2-W resistor, clearly identifying each, as to value and power dissipation. Learn to identify the sizes and the associated power dissipation.

(b) In Table 1.3, fill in the required information concerning the five 2-W resistors provided.

The sixth column of Table 1.3 requires that you measure the resistance of each resistor. Do this using each meter in turn. Then compare these values, but record only that resistance value indicated by the DMM in the column labeled "Measured Value."

TABLE 1.3

Color Bands 1 2 3 4	Nominal Resistance Value	Tolerance (%)	Maximum Resistance	Minimum Resistance	Measured Value	Falls Within Specified Tolerance (Yes/No)

(c) Guess the resistance of your body and record the value in Table 1.4. Now measure your body resistance by firmly holding the multimeter leads, one in each hand. Record the measured resistance and compare it to your guess. If 10 mA are "lethal," what voltage would be required to produce this current in your body?

_____

TABLE 1.4

Guessed Body Resistance	
Measured Body Resistance	
Lethal Voltage	

Part 2

(a) Connect the DMM across terminals A and B (see Fig. 1.2 for subscript explanation) of the power supply. Turn on the supply and adjust the output voltage V_{AB} to zero. Using the VOM, measure the voltages V_{AB}, V_{AG}, and V_{BG} and record in Table 1.5. Now increase the voltage V_{AB} in 4-V steps, each time setting the initial voltage with the DMM and then measuring V_{AB}, V_{AG}, and V_{BG} with the VOM. Record the values at each setting in Table 1.5. Note that the DMM is being used as a standard or reference.

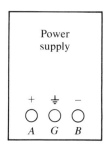

If the supply has a built-in meter, do not use it. The voltage from A to B will be referred to as V_{AB} and from A to G as V_{AG}. In addition, if V_{AB} is positive, then V_{BA} is negative.

FIG. 1.2

TABLE 1.5

V_{AB} Set with DMM	V_{AB}	V_{AG}	V_{BG}	% Accuracy of Reading for V_{AB}	% Accuracy of FSD for V_{AB}
0 V					
4 V					
8 V					
12 V					
16 V					
20 V					
24 V					

Since we are using the DMM as our standard (due to its greater accuracy), we can now calculate the percent accuracy of reading.

$$\frac{\% \text{ Accuracy}}{\text{of reading}} = \frac{|\text{ VOM reading} - \text{DMM reading }|}{\text{DMM reading}} \times 100 \tag{1.2}$$

Do this calculation for each of the readings for V_{AB} (except for zero of course). Record the calculated values in Table 1.5. Show at least one sample calculation below.

Why do the percentages differ?

How close to the given accuracy do they come?

Meters are defined as having a particular percent accuracy of full scale deflection FSD. It is an indication of how accurate the reading will be for a particular scale. For a ±3% FSD meter used on a 10-V scale, the possible range of indication is ±0.3 V or within a 0.6-V range.

For a particular reading the percent accuracy of FSD can be determined from

$$\frac{\%\ \text{Accuracy}}{\text{of FSD}} = \frac{|\ \text{VOM reading} - \text{DMM reading}\ |}{\text{FSD (VOM)}} \times 100 \qquad (1.3)$$

Assuming a ±3% FSD for the VOM (if known, check against the provided value), determine the percent accuracy of FSD for each reading of V_{AB}. Record in Table 1.5. Comment below on whether all of the readings fall within the percent accuracy of FSD.

(b) In this part we will use the DMM as an ohmmeter to measure the resistance of each voltage range of the VOM when used as a voltmeter. This is important since this resistance affects the circuit that the voltmeter is connected into, and must be taken into consideration. This is called the *loading effect* of an instrument or a circuit. The resistance of any range is calculated:

$$\begin{array}{c} R_M\ \text{(resistance of} \\ \text{the meter range)} \end{array} = \begin{pmatrix} \text{sensitivity in} \\ \text{ohms/volt} \end{pmatrix}\begin{pmatrix} \text{maximum value of} \\ \text{the chosen range} \end{pmatrix} \qquad (1.4)$$

For example, if the sensitivity of a voltmeter is $1000\ \Omega/V$ and the chosen range is $0-10\ V$, then the internal resistance of the meter range is determined by

$$R_M = (1000)(10) = 10,000\ \Omega$$

Record the ohms/volt sensitivity of your VOM in Fig. 1.3.

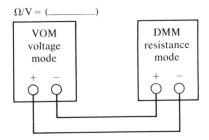

FIG. 1.3

Record the various VOM sensitivity voltage ranges of the VOM in Table 1.6 starting with lowest range first. Calculate the total resistance of each range using Eq. (1.4) and record in Table 1.6 in the column labeled "Calculated Value."

TABLE 1.6

Range	Resistance R_M	
	Calculated Value	Measured Value

Set the VOM to the lowest range and measure the resistance with the DMM. See Fig. 1.3. Record in Table 1.6. Do the same for each subsequent range.

How do the measured values compare to the calculated values?

Part 3

(a) Construct the network of Fig. 1.4. Note that the VOM is in series with

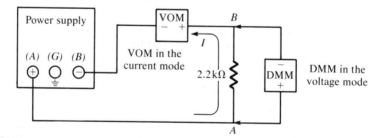

FIG. 1.4

the 2.2-kΩ resistor for the current measurement and the DMM is in parallel for the voltage measurement.

Increase the power supply voltage from 0 to 24 V in 4-V steps. Read the voltmeter and milliammeter at each setting. Use the DMM reading for setting the supply, since the voltage across the resistor is the same as V_{AB}. The voltage drop across the VOM is assumed to be 0 V in the milliammeter mode. Record your readings in Table 1.7.

(b) Replace the 2.2-kΩ resistor with the 220 resistor and repeat the above procedure. Record your results in Table 1.7.

TABLE 1.7

Voltage V_{AB}	Current I (mA)	
	2200 Ω	**220 Ω**
4 V		
8 V		
12 V		
16 V		
20 V		
24 V		

Plot the data from Table 1.7 on Graph 1.1 using the voltage as the ordinate and the current as abscissa. Clearly indicate each curve.

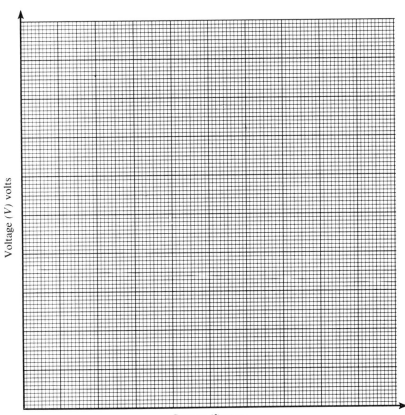

Graph 1.1

Current *(I)* amps

Voltage *(V)* volts

What noticeable differences are there between the two plots?

The slope of the curves is directly related to the resistance value

$$R = \frac{\Delta V}{\Delta I} = m \text{ (slope)} \tag{1.5}$$

In order to determine R (or the slope) from the curves, simply define a range for V (say from 8 to 12 V) and determine the corresponding range for I. Substitution into Eq. (1.5) will provide the desired value.

For each curve of Graph 1.1, calculate R using the 8- to 12-V range and compare to the measured value of the resistor.

2200 Ω resistor: $R_{\text{calculated}} = $ _____

$R_{\text{measured}} = $ _____

220 Ω resistor: $R_{\text{calculated}} = $ _____

$R_{\text{measured}} = $ _____

PROBLEMS

1. What are the ohmic values and tolerances of the following carbon resistors?

TABLE 1.8

Color Bands				Numerical Value	Tolerance
1	**2**	**3**	**4**		
Brown	Black	Blue	Gold		
Yellow	Violet	Orange	Gold		
Brown	Gray	Gold	None		
Red	Yellow	Silver	Gold		
Green	Brown	Green	Silver		
Green	Blue	Black	None		

2. A voltmeter has an accuracy of $\pm 5\%$ of FSD. What is the possible span of the meter reading according to the manufacturer's tolerance if it reads the following voltages: (a) 1 V on the 10-V scale; (b) 10 V on the 10-V scale; and (c) 20 V on the 50-V scale?

3. For best results or accuracy, should you try to obtain a reading as far up-scale as possible? Explain.

OBJECT

To become familiar with the branch-, mesh-, and nodal-analysis techniques.

EQUIPMENT REQUIRED

Resistors

1—1.2 kΩ

2—2.2 kΩ, 3.3 kΩ

Instruments

1—DMM or VOM

2*—dc Power supplies 0–30 V, 0–500 mA (minimum)

*The unavailability of two supplies will simply require that two groups work together.

EQUIPMENT ISSUED

TABLE 6.1

Item	Manufacturer and Model No.	Laboratory Serial No.
DMM or VOM		
Power Supply		
Power Supply		

TABLE 6.2

Resistors	
Nominal Value	Measured Value
1.2 kΩ	1.15 kΩ
2.2 kΩ	2.2 kΩ
2.2 kΩ	2.1 kΩ
3.3 kΩ	3.1 kΩ
3.3 kΩ	3.0 kΩ

RÉSUMÉ OF THEORY

The branch-, mesh-, and nodal-analysis techniques are used to solve complex networks with a single source, or networks with more than one source that are not in series or parallel.

The branch- and mesh-analysis techniques will determine the currents of the network, while the nodal-analysis approach will provide the potential levels of the nodes of the network with respect to some reference.

The application of each technique follows a sequence of steps, each of which will result in a set of equations with the desired unknowns. An application of determinants or other mathematical procedures will then provide the results required.

PROCEDURE

Part 1

(a) Construct the network of Fig. 6.1. Insert the measured values of the resistors.

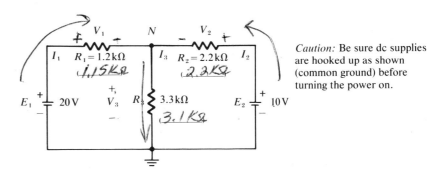

FIG. 6.1

Caution: Be sure dc supplies are hooked up as shown (common ground) before turning the power on.

(b) Using branch-current analysis, calculate the current through each branch of the network of Fig. 6.1. Use the measured resistor values.

$$-20V + (1.15K)(I_1) + (3.1K)(I_3) = 0$$
$$-10V + (2.2K)(I_2) + (3.1K)(I_3) = 0$$
$$I_1 + I_2 - I_3 = 0$$

$$\begin{vmatrix} 20 & 0 & 3.1 \\ 10 & 2.2 & 3.1 \\ 0 & 1 & -1 \end{vmatrix} \begin{vmatrix} 20 & 0 \\ 10 & 2.2 \\ 0 & 1 \end{vmatrix}$$

$$1.15K(I_1) + 0\,I_2 + 3.1K(I_3) = 20$$
$$0(I_1) + 2.2K(I_2) + 3.1K(I_3) = 10$$
$$I_1 + I_2 - I_3 = 0$$

$$\begin{vmatrix} 1.15 & 0 & 3.1 \\ 0 & 2.2 & 3.1 \\ 1 & 1 & -1 \end{vmatrix} \begin{vmatrix} 1.15 & 0 \\ 0 & 2.2 \\ 1 & 1 \end{vmatrix}$$

substitute values accordingly

$$1.65 mA = \frac{13}{7.86}$$

$$I_1 = \underline{5.8\,mA}, \quad I_2 = \underline{6.5\,mA}, \quad I_3 = \underline{7.05\,mA}$$

(c) Measure the voltages V_1, V_2, and V_3 and calculate the currents I_1, I_2, and I_3. How do they compare to the results of (b)? Include the direction of each current in Fig. 6.1.

$$V_1 = \underline{5.2\,V}, \quad V_2 = \underline{14.5\,V}, \quad V_3 = \underline{14.5\,V}$$

$$I_1 = \underline{4.5\,mA}, \quad I_2 = \underline{6.4\,mA}, \quad I_3 = \underline{4.5\,mA}$$

(d) Using nodal analysis, determine the nodal voltage for the network of Fig. 6.1. Use the measured resistor values.

$V_N =$ _____

(e) How do the results of (d) correspond with the measurements of (c)?

Part 2

(a) Construct the network of Fig. 6.2. Insert the measured value of each resistor in the diagram.

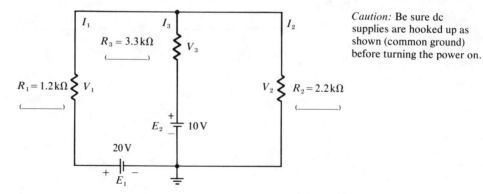

Caution: Be sure dc supplies are hooked up as shown (common ground) before turning the power on.

FIG. 6.2

(b) Using mesh analysis, determine the current through each resistor. Use the measured resistor values.

Mesh currents: $I_1 =$ —————— , $I_2 =$ ——————

Resistor currents: $I_1 =$ —————— , $I_2 =$ —————— ,

$I_3 =$ ——————

(c) Measure the voltages V_1, V_2, and V_3 and calculate the currents I_1, I_2, and I_3. How do they compare to the results of (b)? Include the direction of each current on Fig. 6.2.

$V_1 =$ —————— , $V_2 =$ —————— , $V_3 =$ ——————

$I_1 =$ —————— , $I_2 =$ —————— , $I_3 =$ ——————

(d) Using nodal analysis, determine the nodal voltage ($= V_2$) for the network of Fig. 6.2. Use the measured resistor values.

$V_N =$ _____

(e) Using the results of (c), compare with the results of (d).

V_N (measured) = _____

Part 3

(a) Construct the network of Fig. 6.3. Insert the measured resistor values.

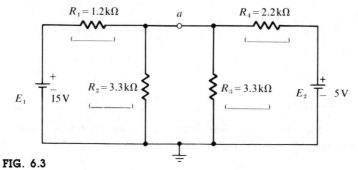

FIG. 6.3

(b) Using nodal analysis, calculate the voltage V_a. Use the measured resistor values.

V_a (calculated) = _____

(c) Measure the voltage V_a and compare with the results of (b).

V_a (measured) = _____

Part 4

(a) Construct the network of Fig. 6.4. Insert the measured resistor values.

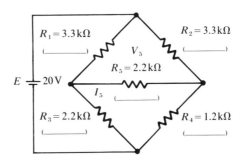

FIG. 6.4

(b) Using any one of the three techniques examined in this experiment, calculate the voltage V_5 and the current I_5. Use the measured resistor values.

V_5 (calculated) = _____ , I_5 (calculated) = _____

(c) Measure the voltage V_5 and compare with the results of (b).

V_5 (measured) = _____

Superposition Principle (dc)

OBJECT

To verify experimentally the superposition principle as applied to dc circuits.

EQUIPMENT REQUIRED

Resistors

1—91 Ω, 220 Ω, 330 Ω

Instruments

1—DMM or VOM

2*—dc Power supplies 0–30 V, 0–500 mA (minimum)

*The unavailability of two power supplies may require that two groups work together.

EQUIPMENT ISSUED

TABLE 7.1

Item	Manufacturer and Model No.	Laboratory Serial No.
DMM or VOM		
Power Supply		
Power Supply		

TABLE 7.2

Resistors	
Nominal Value	Measured Value
91 Ω	
220 Ω	
330 Ω	

RÉSUMÉ OF THEORY

The superposition principle states that the current through, or voltage across, any resistive branch of a multisource network is the algebraic sum of the contributions due to each source acting independently. When the effects of one source are considered, the others are replaced by their internal resistances. Superposition is only effective for linear circuit relationships.

This principle permits one to analyze circuits without resorting to simultaneous equations. Nonlinear effects, such as power, which varies as the square of the current or voltage, cannot be analyzed using this principle.

PROCEDURE

Part 1

(a) Construct the network of Fig. 7.1. Insert the measured value of each resistor.

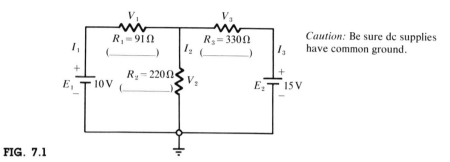

FIG. 7.1

(b) Using superposition and the measured resistor values, calculate the voltages and currents indicated in Table 7.3.

TABLE 7.3   Calculated values for the network of Fig. 7.1

Due to E_1	Due to E_2	Algebraic Sum
$I_1 =$	$I_1 =$	$I_1 =$
$I_2 =$	$I_2 =$	$I_2 =$
$I_3 =$	$I_3 =$	$I_3 =$
$V_1 =$	$V_1 =$	$V_1 =$
$V_2 =$	$V_2 =$	$V_2 =$
$V_3 =$	$V_3 =$	$V_3 =$

(c) Energize the network of Fig. 7.1 and measure the voltages indicated in Table 7.4. Calculate the currents in Table 7.4 using Ohm's law. Note the polarity of the voltages and the direction of the currents on Fig. 7.1.

TABLE 7.4   Measured values for the network of Fig. 7.1

$V_1 =$	
$V_2 =$	
$V_3 =$	
$I_1 =$	
$I_2 =$	
$I_3 =$	

(d) Comment on the results of (b) and (c).

(e) Construct the network of Fig. 7.2. Note that source #2 (E_2) has been removed.

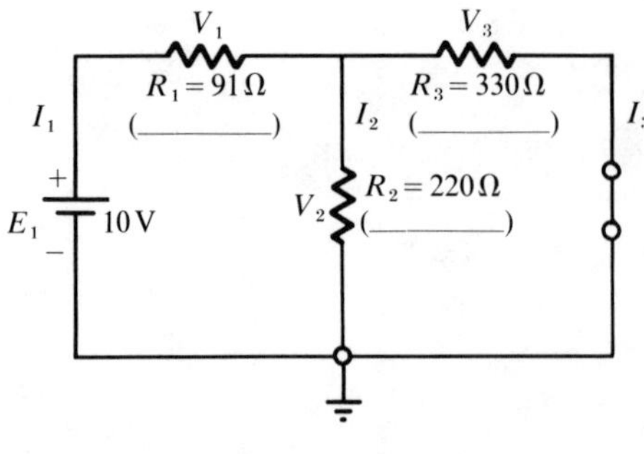

FIG. 7.2

(f) Calculate the currents and voltages in Table 7.5 using the measured resistor values. In addition, include the polarity of the voltages and the direction of the currents on Fig. 7.2.

TABLE 7.5   **Calculated values for the network of Fig. 7.2**

$I_1 =$	
$I_2 =$	
$I_3 =$	
$V_1 =$	
$V_2 =$	
$V_3 =$	

(g) Energize the network of Fig. 7.2 and measure the voltages indicated in Table 7.6. Calculate the currents using Ohm's law. Use measured resistor values.

TABLE 7.6   **Measured values for the network of Fig. 7.2**

$V_1 =$	
$V_2 =$	
$V_3 =$	
$I_1 =$	
$I_2 =$	
$I_3 =$	

(**h**) Compare the results of (f) and (g).

(**i**) Construct the network of Fig. 7.3. Note that source #1 (E_1) has been removed.

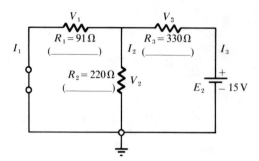

FIG. 7.3

(**j**) Calculate the currents and voltages in Table 7.7 using the measured resistor values. In addition, include the polarity of the voltages and the direction of the currents on Fig. 7.3.

TABLE 7.7   Calculated values for the network of Fig. 7.3

$I_1 =$	
$I_2 =$	
$I_3 =$	
$V_1 =$	
$V_2 =$	
$V_3 =$	

(**k**) Energize the network of Fig. 7.3 and measure the voltages indicated in Table 7.8. Calculate the currents using Ohm's law. Use measured resistor values.

TABLE 7.8   Measured values for the network of Fig. 7.3

$V_1 =$
$V_2 =$
$V_3 =$
$I_1 =$
$I_2 =$
$I_3 =$

(l) Compare the results of (j) and (k).

(m) Find the algebraic sum of the voltages and currents of (f) and (j) and insert in Table 7.9. Repeat for the results of (g) and (k). How do the results compare with those obtained in (b) and (c)?

TABLE 7.9   Algebraic results for the network of Fig. 7.1

Calculated	Measured
$I_1 =$	$I_1 =$
$I_2 =$	$I_2 =$
$I_3 =$	$I_3 =$
$V_1 =$	$V_1 =$
$V_2 =$	$V_2 =$
$V_3 =$	$V_3 =$

(n) Using the results of (g), determine the power delivered to each resistor and insert in Table 7.10. Repeat for the results of (k). Finally, include the results obtained using the measurements of (c) and complete the table.

TABLE 7.10

(g)	(k)	Sum of (g) + (k)	(c)
$P_1 =$	$P_1 =$	$P_1 =$	$P_1 =$
$P_2 =$	$P_2 =$	$P_2 =$	$P_2 =$
$P_3 =$	$P_3 =$	$P_3 =$	$P_3 =$

(o) Referring to the results of (n), comment on the applicability of the superposition theorem to power effects.

Part 2

(a) Construct the network of Fig. 7.4. Insert the measured resistor values.

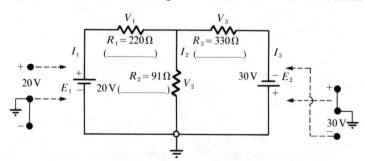

FIG. 7.4

(b) Using the measured resistor values, calculate the voltages V_1, V_2, and V_3 using superposition. Show your work in the space provided.

$V_1 = $ _____ , $V_2 = $ _____ , $V_3 = $ _____

(c) Energize the network of Fig. 7.4 and measure the voltages V_1, V_2, and V_3. Is the superposition principle verified?

$V_1 = $ _____ , $V_2 = $ _____ , $V_3 = $ _____

(d) Using measured resistor values, calculate the voltage V_2 due only to source #1 (E_1). Modify the network and measure the voltage V_2 due only to source #1 (E_1). Be sure to note the polarity of V_2.

V_2 (calculated) = _____ , V_2 (measured) = _____

(e) Repeat (d) for source #2 (E_2).

V_2 (calculated) = _____ , V_2 (measured) = _____

(f) Using the measured results of (d) and (e), determine the voltage V_2 and compare to the results of (c).

V_2 [Part 2 (d) and (e)] = _____ , V_2 [Part 2 (c)] = _____

Thevenin's Theorem and Maximum Power Transfer

Experiment dc

8

OBJECT

To verify Thevenin's theorem and the maximum power transfer principle.

EQUIPMENT REQUIRED

Resistors

1—91 Ω, 220 Ω, 330 Ω, 470 Ω

1—(0–1 kΩ) potentiometer

Instruments

1—DMM or VOM

1—dc Power supply 0–30 V, 0–500 mA (minimum)

EQUIPMENT ISSUED

TABLE 8.1

Item	Manufacturer and Model No.	Laboratory Serial No.
DMM or VOM		
Power Supply		

TABLE 8.2

Resistors	
Nominal Value	Measured Value
91 Ω	
220 Ω	
330 Ω	
470 Ω	

RÉSUMÉ OF THEORY

Through the use of Thevenin's theorem, a complex, two-terminal, linear, multisource dc network can be replaced by one having a single source and resistor.

The Thevenin equivalent circuit consists of a single dc source referred to as the *Thevenin voltage* and a single fixed resistor referred to as the *Thevenin resistance*. The Thevenin voltage is the open-circuit voltage across the terminals in question. The Thevenin resistance is the resistance between these terminals with all of the voltage and current sources replaced by their internal resistances.

If a dc voltage source is to deliver maximum power to a resistor, the resistor must have a value equal to the internal resistance of the source. In a complex network, maximum power transfer to a load will occur when the load resistance is equal to the Thevenin resistance "seen" by the load. For this value, the voltage across the load will be one-half of the Thevenin voltage. In equation form the maximum power is given by

$$P_{\max} = \frac{E_{Th}^2}{4R_{Th}}$$

(8.1)

PROCEDURE

Part 1   Thevenin's Theorem

(a) Insert the measured resistor values into Fig. 8.1 and calculate the Thevenin voltage and resistance for the network to the left of points *a-a'*.

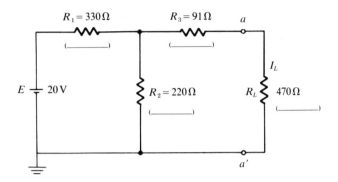

FIG. 8.1

$$E_{Th} = \underline{\hspace{3cm}} , \; R_{Th} = \underline{\hspace{3cm}}$$

(b) Insert the values obtained in (a) into the schematic of Fig. 8.2 and calculate I_L.

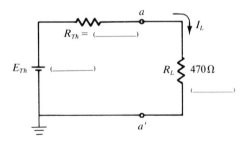

FIG. 8.2

$$I_L = \underline{\hspace{3cm}}$$

(c) Calculate the current I_L in the original network of Fig. 8.1 using series-parallel techniques (use measured resistor values). Compare to the results of (b).

$I_L =$ _____

(d) Construct the network of Fig. 8.1 and measure the voltage V_L. Calculate the current I_L and compare to the results of (b).

I_L (measured) $=$ _____

(e) Determine R_{Th} by constructing the network of Fig. 8.3 and measuring the resistance between points a-a'.

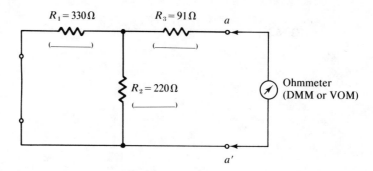

FIG. 8.3

$R_{Th} =$ _____

How does it compare to the value determined in (a)?

(f) Determine E_{Th} by constructing the network of Fig. 8.4 and measuring the open-circuit voltage between points a-a'.

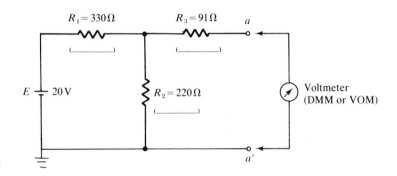

FIG. 8.4

E_{Th} (measured) = _____

How does this value compare to the results of (a)?

(g) Construct the network of Fig. 8.5 and set the values obtained for E_{Th} and R_{Th} in (e) and (f). Use the ohmmeter section of your meters to properly set the potentiometer. Then measure the voltage V_L and calculate the current I_L. Compare to the results of (b) and (c).

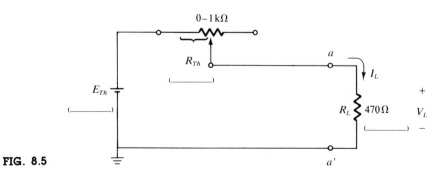

FIG. 8.5

$$V_L = \underline{\hspace{3cm}} , I_L = \underline{\hspace{2.5cm}}$$

Part 2   Maximum Power Transfer

(a) Construct the network of Fig. 8.6 and set the potentiometer to 50 Ω. Measure the voltage across R as you vary R through the following values: 50, 100, 200, 300, 330, 400, 600, 800, and 1000 Ω. Be sure to set the resistance with the ohmmeter section of your meter before each reading. (Remember to disconnect the dc supply when setting the resistance level.) Complete Table 8.3 and plot power (ordinate) versus R (abscissa) on Graph 8.1.

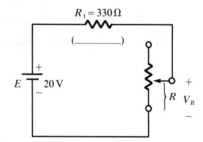

FIG. 8.6

TABLE 8.3

R	V_R	P_R
50 Ω		
100 Ω		
200 Ω		
300 Ω		
R_1(meas)		
400 Ω		
600 Ω		
800 Ω		
1,000 Ω		

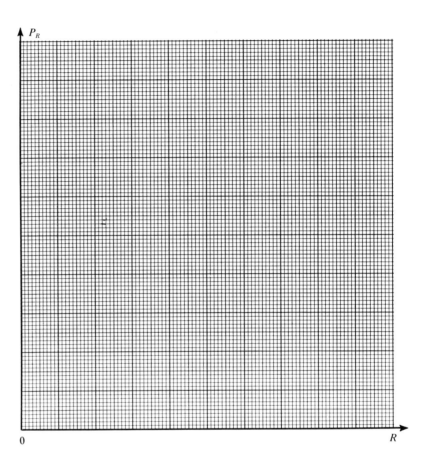

GRAPH 8.1   0

R

(b) Theoretically, for what value of R will the power delivered to R be maximum? $R =$ _____ . Check this value against that obtained from the graph.

In addition, what should the voltage across R be when R is set for maximum power? $V_R =$ _____ . Does your experimental data substantiate this?

(c) Construct the network of Fig. 8.7 and set the potentiometer to 10 Ω. Complete Table 8.4 for each value of R.

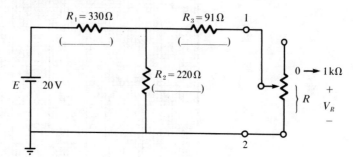

FIG. 8.7

TABLE 8.4

R	V_R	P_R
10 Ω		
50 Ω		
100 Ω		
150 Ω		
200 Ω		
250 Ω		
300 Ω		
350 Ω		
400 Ω		

(d) What value of R would appear to result in a maximum power transfer to the load? How does it compare to the value of R_{Th} determined in Part 1(a)?

$R = $ _____

Part 3

(a) Construct the network of Fig. 8.8. Insert the measured resistor values.

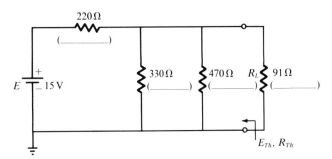

FIG. 8.8

(b) Using *experimental techniques*, determine the maximum power to the resistor R_L. That is, determine E_{Th} and R_{Th} experimentally and then use Eq. (8.1).

$E_{Th} = $ _____ , $R_{Th} = $ _____ , $P_{max} = $ _____

(c) Calculate the values of E_{Th}, R_{Th}, and P_{max} using measured resistor values, and compare to the results of (b).

$E_{Th} =$ _____ , $R_{Th} =$ _____ , $P_{max} =$ _____

(d) Comment on whether $R_L = 91\Omega$ is a poor or excellent choice for maximum power transfer to the load. With $R_L = 91\Omega$ what percent of maximum power is delivered to the load?

Norton's Theorem and Source Conversions

Experiment dc

9

OBJECT

To verify Norton's theorem and the theory of source conversion.

EQUIPMENT REQUIRED

Resistors

1—47 Ω, 220 Ω, 330 Ω, 3.3 kΩ, 10 kΩ

1—(0–1 kΩ) potentiometer

Instruments

1—DMM

1—dc Power supply 0–30 V, 0–500 mA (minimum)

EQUIPMENT ISSUED

TABLE 9.1

Item	Manufacturer and Model No.	Laboratory Serial No.
DMM		
Power Supply		

TABLE 9.2

Resistors	
Nominal Value	**Measured Value**
47 Ω	
220 Ω	
330 Ω	
3.3 kΩ	
10 kΩ	

RÉSUMÉ OF THEORY

Through the use of Thevenin's or Norton's theorem, a complex, two-terminal, linear, multisource dc network can be replaced by a single source and resistor.

The *Norton equivalent circuit* is a single dc current source in parallel with a resistor. The *Norton current* is the short-circuit current between the terminals in question. The *Norton resistance* is the resistance between these terminals with all voltage and current sources replaced by their internal resistances.

The theory of source conversion dictates that the Norton and Thevenin circuits are terminally equivalent and related as follows:

$$\boxed{R_N = R_{Th}} \qquad \boxed{E_{Th} = I_N R_N} \qquad \boxed{I_N = \frac{E_{Th}}{R_{Th}}} \qquad (9.1)$$

Therefore, if you have converted a complex network to its Norton equivalent, it is a simple matter to convert it to a Thevenin equivalent circuit.

PROCEDURE

Part 1

(a) Construct the circuit of Fig. 9.1. Insert the measured values of each resistor.

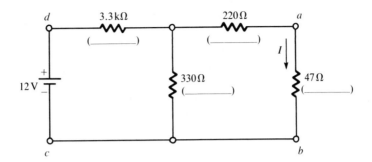

FIG. 9.1

Measure the current through the 47-Ω resistor by measuring the voltage drop across the resistor (V_{ab}) and then calculating the value of I using Ohm's law (use the measured resistor value). Record the value of I.

$V_{ab} =$ _____ , $I =$ _____

In the parts that follow we will show that this same current will result using the Norton equivalent circuit.

(b) Calculate the Norton resistance (R_N) and the Norton current (I_N) so that the Norton equivalent circuit can be found for the network external to the 47-Ω resistor. Use the measured values of the resistors for your calculations. (Show all calculations and be neat.)

Record the calculated values of R_N and I_N in Table 9.3.

TABLE 9.3

Parameter	Calculated	Measured
R_N		
I_N		

(c) Remove the 47-Ω resistor and initially place the DMM set on a high current range across points a-b. Turn on the power and measure the current $I_{a\text{-}b}$ with that scale setting that gives you the most accurate reading. (This is the value of I_N and should be recorded in Table 9.3.) Shut down, physically disconnect the supply from the circuit, and connect a wire across points c-d of the circuit. Change the DMM mode so that it is now operating as an ohmmeter and measure the resistance across points a-b. This is the measured value of R_N. Record this value in Table 9.3. How do the two values of R_N and I_N compare?

Draw the Norton equivalent circuit in the space below. Indicate points a-b, the 47-Ω resistor, and the values of R_N and I_N on the diagram. Use the measured values of R_N and I_N.

(d) Construct the circuit of Fig. 9.2.

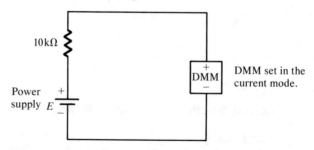

FIG. 9.2

Vary the supply voltage until the DMM indicates the value I_N from (c). Record the value in Fig. 9.3 in the place indicated. Next remove the DMM and, using it as an ohmmeter, set the 0–1-kΩ potentiometer to the value of R_N from (c). Now insert the 0–1-kΩ potentiometer into the circuit of Fig. 9.3.

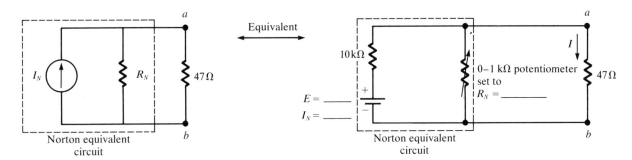

FIG. 9.3

The circuit of Fig. 9.3 is the Norton equivalent circuit, The $0-1$-kΩ potentio-meter is equivalent to R_N and the 10-kΩ resistor in series with the power supply is the equivalent current source. The 10-kΩ resistor was chosen to ensure minimum sensi-tivity on the part of I_N to the smaller resistor values connected in parallel in Fig. 9.3. In other words, $I_N = E/(10\,\text{k}\Omega + R_{\text{network}}) \cong E/10\,\text{k}\Omega$, and therefore approximates an ideal current source.

Measure the voltage V_{ab} and compute I using the measured resistor value.

$V_{ab} = $ _____ , $I = $ _____

How do these values compare to those of (a)?

Part 2

(a) According to the theory of source conversion, the Norton equivalent cir-cuit of Fig. 9.3 can easily be converted to a Thevenin equivalent circuit. Further, if the circuits are completely equivalent the values of V_{ab} and I should remain the same as before. The conversion can be accomplished by first calculating the Thevenin voltage E_{Th} where $E_{Th} = I_N R_N$. Calculate E_{Th}:

$E_{Th} = $ _____

Since $R_{Th} = R_N$ the Thevenin equivalent circuit can now be constructed.
(b) Construct the circuit of Fig. 9.4.

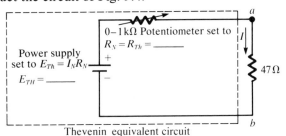

FIG. 9.4   Thevenin equivalent circuit

Now measure the voltage V_{ab} and again compute I. (Use the measured value of the 47-Ω resistor.)

$V_{ab} =$ _____ , $I =$ _____

How do the values of V_{ab} and I compare with those in Part 1(d)?

What does this show?

Summarize your conclusions.

OBJECT

To become familiar with the characteristics of a capacitor in a dc system.

EQUIPMENT REQUIRED

Resistors

2—1.2 kΩ, 100 kΩ

Capacitors

2—100 μF (electrolytic)

Instruments

1—DMM or VOM

1—dc Power supply 0–30 V, 0–500 mA (minimum)

1—Single-pole, single-throw switch

EQUIPMENT ISSUED

TABLE 10.1

Item	Manufacturer and Model No.	Laboratory Serial No.
DMM or VOM		
Power Supply		

TABLE 10.2

Resistors	
Nominal Value	**Measured Value**
$1.2\,k\Omega$	
$1.2\,k\Omega$	
$100\,k\Omega$	
$100\,k\Omega$	

RÉSUMÉ OF THEORY

The *resistor* dissipates electrical energy in the form of heat. In contrast, the *capacitor* is a component that stores electrical energy in the form of an electrical field. The capacitance of a capacitor is a function of its geometry and the dielectric used. Dielectric materials (insulators) are rated by their ability to support an electric field in terms of a figure called the dielectric constant (k). Dry air is the standard dielectric for purposes of reference and is assigned the value of unity. Mica, with a dielectric constant of 6, has six times the capacitance of a similarly constructed air capacitor.

One of the most common capacitors is the parallel-plate type. The capacitance (in farads) is determined by

$$C = k\frac{A}{d} \tag{10.1}$$

where k = dielectric constant (9×10^9), A = area of the plates (m^2), and d = distance between the plates (m). By changing any one of the three parameters, one can easily change the capacitance.

The dielectric constant is not to be confused with the dielectric strength of a material, which is given in volts/unit length and is a measure of the maximum stress that a dielectric can withstand before it breaks down and loses its insulator characteristics.

In a dc circuit, the volt-ampere characteristics of a capacitor in the steady-state mode are such that the capacitor prevents the flow of dc current but will charge up to a dc voltage. Essentially, therefore, the characteristics of a capacitor in the steady-state mode are those of an open circuit. The charge Q stored by a capacitor is given by

$$\boxed{Q = CV} \tag{10.2}$$

where C = capacitance and V = voltage impressed across the capacitor.
Capacitors in series behave like resistors in parallel:

$$\boxed{\frac{1}{C_T} = \frac{1}{C_1} + \frac{1}{C_2} + \frac{1}{C_3} + \frac{1}{C_4}} \tag{10.3}$$

Capacitors in parallel behave like resistors in series:

$$\boxed{C_T = C_1 + C_2 + C_3 + C_4} \tag{10.4}$$

The energy stored by a capacitor is determined by

$$\boxed{W = \frac{1}{2} CV^2} \ \text{(joules, J)} \tag{10.5}$$

For the network of Fig. 10.1 the capacitor will, for all practical purposes, charge up to E volts in *five* time constants where a time constant (τ) is defined by

$$\boxed{\tau = RC} \tag{10.6}$$

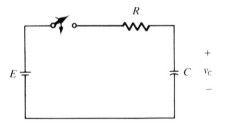

FIG. 10.1

In one time constant the voltage v_C will charge up to 63.2% of its final value, in 2τ—86.5%, 3τ—95.1%, 4τ—98.1%, and 5τ—99.3%.

PROCEDURE

Part 1

(a) Construct the network of Fig. 10.2.

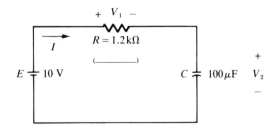

FIG. 10.2

(b) Calculate the steady-state value (defined by a period of time greater than five constants) of the current I and the voltages V_1 and V_2.

$I = $ _____ , $V_1 = $ _____ , $V_2 = $ _____

(c) Measure the voltages V_1 and V_2 and calculate the current I from Ohm's law and compare to the results of (b).

$I = $ _____ , $V_1 = $ _____ , $V_2 = $ _____

(d) Calculate the energy stored by the capacitor.

$W = $ _____ J

(e) Carefully disconnect the supply and measure the voltage across the capacitor. Is there a reading? Why?

$V_C = $ _____

(f) Short the capacitor terminals with a lead. Explain any resulting effect. Why was it necessary to perform this step?

Part 2

(a) Construct the network of Fig. 10.3.

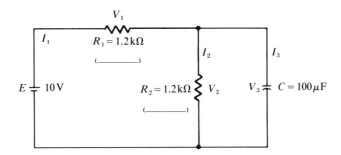

FIG. 10.3

(b) Using ideal elements, calculate the theoretical steady-state levels of the following quantities. (The measured resistor values should be used.)

$I_1 = $ _____ , $I_2 = $ _____ , $I_3 = $ _____

$V_1 = $ _____ , $V_2 = $ _____ , $V_3 = $ _____

(c) Energize the system and measure the voltages V_1, V_2, and V_3. Calculate the currents I_1 and I_2 from Ohm's law and the current I_3 from Kirchoff's current law. Compare the results with (b).

$V_1 = $ _____ , $V_2 = $ _____ , $V_3 = $ _____

$I_1 = $ _____ , $I_2 = $ _____ , $I_3 = $ _____

Part 3

(a) Construct the network of Fig. 10.4.

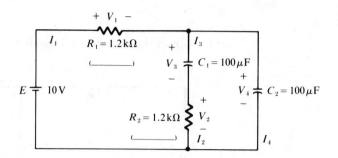

FIG. 10.4

(b) Assuming ideal elements, calculate the theoretical steady-state levels of the following quantities (use the measured resistance levels):

$I_1 =$ _____ , $I_2 =$ _____ , $I_3 =$ _____ ,
$I_4 =$ _____
$V_1 =$ _____ , $V_2 =$ _____ , $V_3 =$ _____ ,
$V_4 =$ _____

(c) Energize the system and measure the voltages V_1, V_2, V_3, and V_4. Calculate the currents I_1 and I_2 from Ohm's law and determine I_3 and I_4 from Kirchhoff's current law. Compare the results with (b).

$V_1 =$ _____ , $V_2 =$ _____ , $V_3 =$ _____ ,
$V_4 =$ _____
$I_1 -$ _____ , $I_2 =$ _____ , $I_3 -$ _____ ,
$I_4 =$ _____

Part 4   Charging Network

(a) Calculate the time constant for the network of Fig. 10.5. Use the measured resistance value.

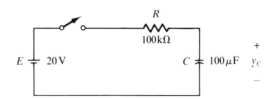

FIG. 10.5

$$\tau = \underline{\hspace{2cm}}$$

(b) Discharge the capacitor and be sure the switch is in the open position. Then close the switch and note how many seconds pass before the voltage v_C reaches 63.2% of its final value or $(0.632)(20) = 12.64\,\text{V}$.

$$t_{(63.2\%)} = \underline{\hspace{2cm}}$$

You will note that the t is somewhat larger than you expected from the calculations of (a). This is due to the leakage resistance typically present in electrolytic capacitances of this capacitance level.

(c) An equivalent capacitance can be defined, however, that will permit an examination of the charging phase of a capacitor when applied to a dc source. It will be determined from

$$\boxed{C_{eq} = \frac{t}{R}} \qquad \begin{array}{l}(t = \text{time required to reach the 63.2\% level}) \\ (R = \text{measured value})\end{array} \qquad \textbf{(10.7)}$$

as derived from the time constant equation $\tau = RC$.

Calculate the equivalent capacitance for the configuration of Fig. 10.5.

$$C_{eq_1} = \underline{\hspace{2cm}}$$

Repeat the above determination for the other capacitor.

$$C_{eq_2} = \underline{\hspace{2cm}}$$

From this point on, simply assume each capacitor has a capacitance equivalent to C_{eq} and the data obtained for this experiment should be quite satisfactory.

(d) Determine the time constant and charging time for the network of Fig. 10.6. Use the measured resistance levels and C_{eq} for each capacitor.

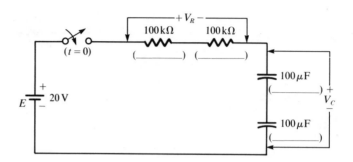

FIG. 10.6

$\tau =$ _____ , $5\tau =$ _____

(e) Using a watch, record (to the best of your ability), the voltage across the resistors at the time intervals noted in Table 10.3 after the switch is closed. Complete the table for V_C using the fact that $V_C = E - V_R$.

TABLE 10.3

t (s)	5	10	15	20	25	30	35	40	45	50	55	60
V_R												
V_C												

(f) In one time constant, the voltage V_C should be 63.2% of its final steady-state value of 20 V. Is this verified by the data of (e)?

(g) Plot the curves of v_R and v_C versus time, on Graph 10.1.

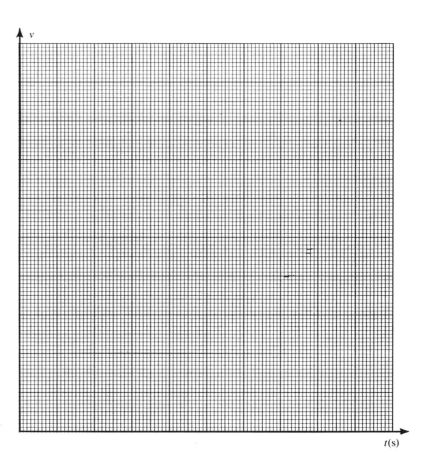

GRAPH 10.1

(**h**) Construct the network of Fig. 10.7. Insert the measured resistance level and each C_{eq}.

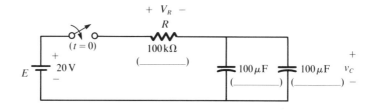

FIG. 10.7

Repeat (d) through (g) and complete Table 10.4

$\tau =$ _____ , $5\tau =$ _____

TABLE 10.4

t (s)	10	20	30	40	50	60	70	80	90	100	110	120
V_R												
V_C												

Plot the curves of v_R and v_C versus time, on Graph 10.2.

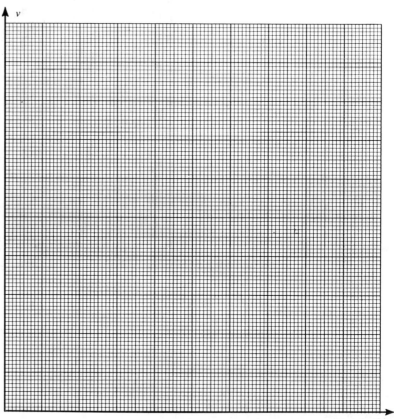

GRAPH 10.2 t(s)

Does the data verify the theoretical conclusions?

R-L Circuits with a dc Source Voltage

Experiment dc

11

OBJECT

To investigate the response of R-L circuits to a dc voltage input.

EQUIPMENT REQUIRED

Resistors

1—470 Ω, 1 kΩ

Inductors

1—5 H

Instruments

1—VOM

1—DMM

1—dc Power supply 0–30 V, 0–500 mA (minimum)

Miscellaneous

1—SPST switch

1—NE-2 neon glow lamp

EQUIPMENT ISSUED

TABLE 11.1

Item	Manufacturer and Model No.	Laboratory Serial No.
VOM		
DMM		
Power Supply		

TABLE 11.2

Resistors	
Nominal Value	Measured Value
470 Ω	
1 kΩ	

RÉSUMÉ OF THEORY

The inductor, like the capacitor, is an energy-storing device. The capacitor stores energy in an electric field; the inductor stores it in a magnetic field. The energy stored by an inductor is given by

$$W = \frac{1}{2}LI^2 \qquad \text{(joules, J)} \tag{11.1}$$

In any circuit containing an inductor, the voltage across that inductor is determined by the inductance (L) and the rate of change of the current through the inductor:

$$V_L = L\,\frac{\text{change of current}}{\text{change of time}} = L\,\frac{\Delta i}{\Delta t} \tag{11.2}$$

If the current is constant (as in a dc circuit), $\Delta i/\Delta t = 0$, and the only voltage drop across the inductor is due to the dc resistance of the wire that makes up the inductor. Because an inductor has a dc resistance, we draw it schematically as shown in Fig. 11.1. It is shown as a resistor in series with a pure inductor.

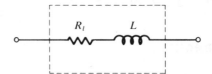

FIG. 11.1

Inductors in series or parallel behave like resistors in series or parallel so that for four inductors in series,

$$L_T = L_1 + L_2 + L_3 + L_4$$ **(11.3)**

and for four inductors in parallel,

$$\frac{1}{L_T} = \frac{1}{L_1} + \frac{1}{L_2} + \frac{1}{L_3} + \frac{1}{L_4}$$ **(11.4)**

PROCEDURE

Part 1

Construct the circuit of Fig. 11.2. Insert the measured value of R_1 and R_l.

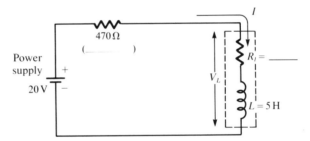

FIG. 11.2

(a) Assuming that the inductor in the circuit of Fig. 11.2 is a pure inductor ($R_l = 0\,\Omega$), calculate the current (I) and the voltage (V_L).

$I =$ _____ , $V_L =$ _____

(b) Measure I and V_L. (I is to be measured by measuring the voltage across the 470-Ω resistor and calculating I using Ohm's law.)

I (measured) = _____ , $V_L =$ _____

Calculate R_l.

$R_l =$ _____

How does the value of R_l in (b) compare with the measured value?

Is it possible for a practical inductor to have $R_l = 0$? Explain.

Part 2   Parallel R-L dc Circuit

Construct the circuit of Fig. 11.3. Insert the measured values of each resistor.

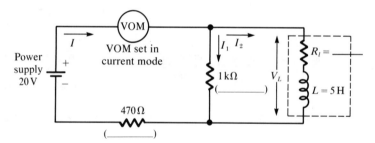

FIG. 11.3

(a) Calculate I assuming an ideal inductor ($R_l = 0\,\Omega$). Use measured resistor values.

$I =$ _____

For I to have the theoretically calculated value, what assumptions must one make about the power supply?

(b) Measure I, I_1, and I_2. (I is read on the VOM, measure V_L and calculate I_1 by dividing by the measured value of the 1-kΩ resistor, and $I_2 = I - I_1$.)

$I = $ _____ , $I_1 = $ _____ , $I_2 = $ _____

Now use the value of I_2 to calculate R_l. Record below.

$R_l = $ _____

How does this value compare to the measured value?

Part 3   Induced Voltage in an Inductor

(a) Take your power supply and put it in series with the supply of another squad as shown in Fig. 11.4.

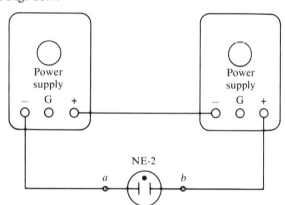

FIG. 11.4

Then place a glow lamp (NE-2) as shown in Fig. 11.4. Vary the voltage of both supplies until the lamp lights. Measure the voltage V_{ab}.

$V_{ab} = $ _____

This is the voltage required to fire the lamp. Repeat the above for the lamp of the other squad.

(b) Return the other supply and construct the circuit of Fig. 11.5.

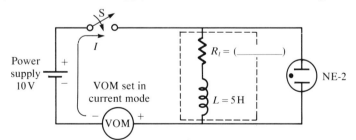

FIG. 11.5

Close the switch (S) and measure the current (*I*) in the circuit. *Note:* Do not leave the switch closed for a long period of time.

$I =$ _____

Does the lamp light with the switch in the on (closed) position?

Now open the switch and note the effect on the lamp. Describe what happens.

When the source current *I* was available, a magnetic field was established linking the windings of the inductor. A steady-state condition was reached where the voltage across the coil was essentially equal to the input voltage *E*. When the switch was opened and the source current removed, the magnetic field linking the inductor collapsed and established a rapidly decaying current through the inductor and neon lamp. Through Eq. (11.2), a large voltage V_L was established that could light the neon bulb for a period of time determined by how long the *rapid* decay continued.

Essentially, the current dropped from the level *I* determined earlier to zero. This change of current is referred to as Δi in the equation $V_L = L(\Delta i / \Delta t)$. Assuming V_L to be the value determined earlier to light the neon bulb, we can calculate the switching time Δt for the current to drop to zero.

$\Delta t =$ _____

What is the effect on Δt of making the inductance larger? Comment accordingly.

An automobile ignition coil (an inductor) has an inductance of 5 H. The initial current is 2 A, and $\Delta t = 0.5$ ms. Calculate the induced voltage at the spark plug.

$$V_L = \underline{\hspace{2cm}}$$

OBJECT

To design and test a dc ammeter and voltmeter.

EQUIPMENT REQUIRED

Resistors

1—10 Ω, 47 Ω

2—100 kΩ

1—(0–10 kΩ) potentiometer

Instruments

1—VOM

1—DMM

1—1-mA, 1000-Ω d'Arsonval meter movement

1—dc Power supply 0–30 V, 0–500 mA (minimum)

EQUIPMENT ISSUED

TABLE 12.1

Item	Manufacturer and Model No.	Laboratory Serial No.
VOM		
DMM		
Power Supply		

TABLE 12.2

Resistors	
Nominal Value	Measured Value
10 Ω	
47 Ω	
100 kΩ	
100 kΩ	

RÉSUMÉ OF THEORY

The basic meter movement is a current-sensitive device. Its basic construction consists of a coil suspended in a magnetic field with a pointer attached to it. When current is passed through the coil, an interaction of magnetic fields will cause the coil to rotate on its axis. The attached pointer will then indicate a particular angular displacement. This angle is proportional to the magnitude of the current through the coil. D'Arsonval meter movements are delicate and sensitive dc milliammeters or microammeters. They are the building blocks used in the design and construction of dc voltmeters and ammeters.

A dc movement (d'Arsonval) can be used to construct a dc voltmeter by connecting a resistor in series with the movement, as shown in Fig. 12.1(a). This series resistor is called the *multiplier*. An ammeter [Fig. 12.1(b)] is constructed by placing a resistor in parallel with the meter movement. This resistor is called the *shunt* resistor.

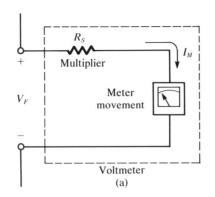 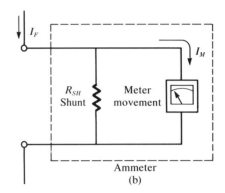

FIG. 12.1

Voltmeter (a)

Ammeter (b)

The value of R_S can be calculated as follows:

$$R_S = \frac{V_F}{I_M} - R_M$$

The value of R_{SH} can be calculated as follows:

$$R_{SH} = \left(\frac{I_M}{I_F - I_M}\right)(R_M)$$

(12.1)

Where

R_S = multiplier resistor

R_{SH} = shunt resistor

I_M = full scale deflection current of the meter movement

R_M = internal resistance of the meter movement

V_F = maximum value of the voltage to be measured for the range being designed

I_F = maximum value of the current to be measured for the range being designed

Example: Using a 0–5-mA meter movement with an internal resistance of 5 kΩ, design (a) 0–50-V voltmeter, and (b) 0–100-mA milliammeter.

Given

$$I_M = 5\,\text{mA}$$
$$R_M = 5\,\text{k}\Omega$$

then

(a) $\quad V_F = 50\,\text{V}$

$$R_S = \frac{50}{5 \times 10^{-3}} - 5 \times 10^3 = 5\,\text{k}\Omega$$

(Note Fig. 12.2a.)

(b) $\quad I_F = 100\,\text{mA}$

$$R_{SH} = \left[\frac{5 \times 10^{-3}}{(100 \times 10^{-3}) - (5 \times 10^{-3})}\right](5 \times 10^3) = 263\,\Omega$$

(Note Fig. 12.2b.)

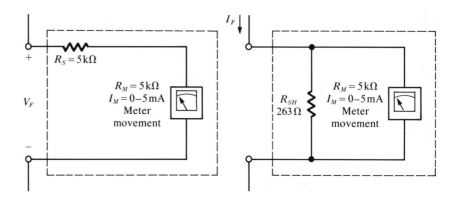

FIG. 12.2

The current sensitivity of a meter is a measure of the current necessary to obtain a full-scale deflection of the meter movement. The inverse of current sensitivity of a voltmeter is the ohm/volt sensitivity of the meter. Therefore, the dc multirange voltmeter, with a 1000-ohm/volt sensitivity, has a current sensitivity of 1/1000, or 1 mA. The VOM, with a 20,000-ohm/volt sensitivity for dc, has a current sensitivity of 1/20,000, or 50 μA.

The accuracy in percent of the full-scale reading indicates the maximum error that will occur in the meter. The Simpson 377 dc voltmeter has an accuracy of $\pm 5\%$ of full-scale. Thus, when set on the 100-V scale, the reading may be in error ± 5 V at any point on the scale. For maximum accuracy, therefore, always choose a scale setting that will give a reading (meter deflection) as close to full-scale as possible.

PROCEDURE

Part 1   Design of a dc Voltmeter

(a) Use the 1000-Ω, 1-mA meter movement to design a 0–10 V dc voltmeter using the appropriate variable resistor. Ask the instructor to check your design before proceeding. Show all calculations.

$R_S = $ _____

Connect your newly constructed voltmeter in parallel with a voltage source and the DMM as shown in Fig. 12.3. Set the variable resistor with your DMM.

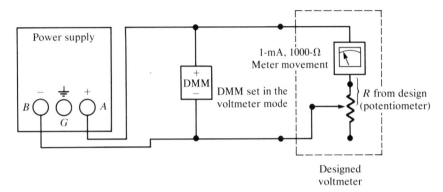

FIG. 12.3

Now vary the power supply from 0 to 10 V in 1-V steps, and record your readings in Table 12.3.

TABLE 12.3

DMM	Designed Voltmeter
1 V	
2 V	
3 V	
4 V	
5 V	
6 V	
7 V	
8 V	
9 V	
10 V	

Calculate the percent accuracy of the reading of your voltmeter at three different readings: 1 V, 5 V, and 10 V.

$$\text{Percent accuracy} = \left[\frac{\left| \left(\begin{array}{c} \text{designed} \\ \text{voltmeter} \\ \text{reading} \end{array} \right) - \left(\begin{array}{c} \text{DMM} \\ \text{reading} \end{array} \right) \right|}{\begin{array}{c} \text{DMM} \\ \text{reading} \end{array}} \right] \times 100\%$$

Percent accuracy at 1 V = _____

Percent accuracy at 5 V = _____

Percent accuracy at 10 V = _____

What do you conclude from the above results?

What is the sensitivity of your voltmeter? _____

Part 2   Design of a dc Milliammeter

Use the meter movement (1-mA, 1000-Ω) to design a 100-mA milliammeter. Let the instructor check your design before proceeding. Then connect it into the circuit shown in Fig. 12.4 and compare its reading against that of the multirange dc milliammeter set

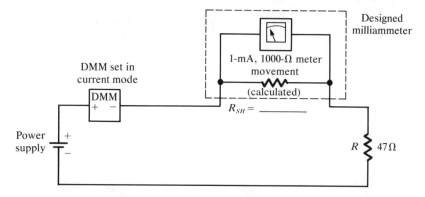

FIG. 12.4

on the proper scale. Start with the voltage control set to zero and increase it so that the current varies from 0 to 100 mA and in 10-mA steps. Use the DMM as the standard. Record the data in Table 12.4. Show your calculations.

R_{SH} = _____

TABLE 12.4

DMM	Designed Milliammeter
10 mA	
20 mA	
30 mA	
40 mA	
50 mA	
60 mA	
70 mA	
80 mA	
90 mA	
100 mA	

Calculate the percent accuracy of the reading of your milliammeter at three different readings: 10 mA, 50 mA, and 100 mA. Use the equation given in Part 1.

Percent accuracy at 10 mA = _____

Percent accuracy at 50 mA = _____

Percent accuracy at 100 mA = _____

What conclusions do you draw from the above results?

Part 3   Meter Loading Effects

(a) Construct the circuit of Fig. 12.5.

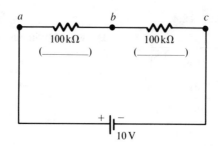

FIG. 12.5

What is the theoretical value of the voltage V_{ab}? Use measured resistor values.

$V_{ab} = $ _____

(b) Read the voltage V_{ab} using the DMM and the VOM on the 10-V scale.

V_{ab} (DMM) = _____ , V_{ab} (VOM) = _____

(c) The DMM has an internal impedance of 11 MΩ or greater and can be considered an open circuit across the 100-kΩ resistors. The VOM, however, has an ohm/volt rating of 20,000 and therefore an internal resistance of (10 V)(20,000 Ω/V) = 200 kΩ on the 10-V scale. Using this internal resistance value, determine the voltage V_{ab} and compare with the results of (b).

V_{ab} (calculated) = _____ , V_{ab} [Part 3 (b)] = _____

(d) Will the 50-V scale of the VOM give a better reading? Record below and note any disadvantages of using this higher scale.

V_{ab} (50-V scale) = _____

(e) If the resistors were replaced by 1-kΩ values, would there be an improvement in the readings of the VOM? Show why with a sample calculation.

PROBLEMS

1. An ammeter with an accuracy of ±3% of full-scale reads 2.1 A when set on the 5-A scale. Within what range of values (about 2.1 A) is this meter accurate?

2. A meter has an ohm/volt sensitivity of 100,000. What is its current sensitivity in microamperes?

Wheatstone Bridge and Δ–Y Conversions

Experiment
dc

13

OBJECT

To become familiar with the Wheatstone bridge and Δ–Y conversions.

EQUIPMENT REQUIRED

Resistors

1—91 Ω

2—220 Ω

3—330 Ω, 1 kΩ

1—(0–1 kΩ) potentiometer

1—Unmarked fixed resistor in the range
47 Ω–200 Ω

Instruments

1—DMM or VOM

1—dc Power supply 0–30 V, 0–500 mA
(minimum)

1—Commercial Wheatstone bridge (if available)

EQUIPMENT ISSUED

TABLE 13.1

Item	Manufacturer and Model No.	Laboratory Serial No.
DMM or VOM		
Power Supply		
Wheatstone Bridge		

TABLE 13.2

Resistors					
Nominal Value	Measured Value	Nominal Value	Measured Value	Nominal Value	Measured Value
91 Ω		330 Ω		1 kΩ	
220 Ω		330 Ω		1 kΩ	
220 Ω		330 Ω		1 kΩ	

RÉSUMÉ OF THEORY

The Wheatstone bridge is an instrument used to make precision measurements of unknown resistance levels. The basic configuration appears in Fig. 13.1. The unknown resistance is R_x, and R_1, R_2, and R_3 are precision resistors of known value.

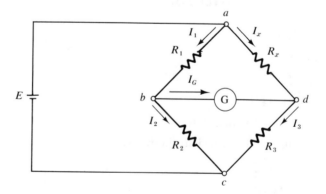

FIG. 13.1

The network is balanced when the galvanometer (G) has a zero-level indication.

We are aware from circuit theory that if $I_G = 0$ A, the voltage V_{bd} is zero and

$$V_{ab} = V_{ad} \qquad \text{and} \qquad V_{bc} = V_{dc}$$

By substitution,

$$I_1R_1 = I_xR_x \qquad\qquad\qquad (13.1)$$

and

$$I_2R_2 = I_3R_3 \qquad\qquad\qquad (13.2)$$

Solving Eq. (13.1) for I_1 yields

$$I_1 = \frac{I_xR_x}{R_1}$$

Substituting I_1 for I_2 and I_x for I_3 in Eq. (13.2), we have

$$I_1R_2 = I_xR_3 \qquad \text{or} \qquad \left(\frac{I_xR_x}{R_1}\right)(R_2) = I_xR_3$$

Canceling I_x from both sides and solving for R_x, we obtain

$$R_x = \frac{R_1}{R_2}R_3 \qquad\qquad\qquad (13.3)$$

or, in the ratio form,

$$\boxed{\frac{R_1}{R_2} = \frac{R_x}{R_3}} \qquad\qquad\qquad (13.4)$$

In the commercial Wheatstone bridge, R_1 and R_2 are variable in decade steps so that the ratio R_1/R_2 is a decimal or integral multiplier. R_3 is a continuous variable resistor, such as a slide-wire rheostat. Before the unknown resistor is connected to the terminals of the commercial bridge, the R_1/R_2 ratio (called the *factor of the ratio arms*) is adjusted for that particular unknown resistor. After the resistor is connected, R_3 is adjusted until there is no detectable current indicated by the galvanometer. (Galvanometer sensitivities are usually 10^{-10} A or better.) The unknown resistance value is the ratio factor times the R_3 setting.

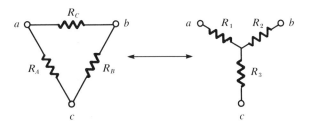

FIG. 13.2

There are certain circuit configurations in which the resistors do not appear to be in series or parallel. Under these conditions, it is necessary to convert the circuit in question from one form to another. The two circuits to be investigated in this experiment are the delta (Δ) and the wye (Y) both of which appear in Fig. 13.2. To convert a Δ to a Y (or vice versa), we use the following conversion equations:

$$R_1 = \frac{R_A R_C}{R_A + R_B + R_C} \qquad R_2 = \frac{R_B R_C}{R_A + R_B + R_C} \qquad R_3 = \frac{R_A R_B}{R_A + R_B + R_C} \qquad \textbf{(13.5)}$$

$$R_A = \frac{R_1 R_2 + R_1 R_3 + R_2 R_3}{R_2} \qquad R_B = \frac{R_1 R_2 + R_1 R_3 + R_2 R_3}{R_1} \qquad \textbf{(13.6)}$$

$$R_C = \frac{R_1 R_2 + R_1 R_3 + R_2 R_3}{R_3}$$

If

$$R_A = R_B = R_C, \qquad \boxed{R_Y = \frac{R_\Delta}{3}} \qquad \textbf{(13.7)}$$

If

$$R_1 = R_2 = R_3, \qquad \boxed{R_\Delta = \frac{R_Y}{3}} \qquad \textbf{(13.8)}$$

PROCEDURE

Part 1   Wheatstone Bridge Circuit

(a) Construct the network of Fig. 13.3. Insert the measured values of each resistor and set the potentiometer to the maximum resistance setting.

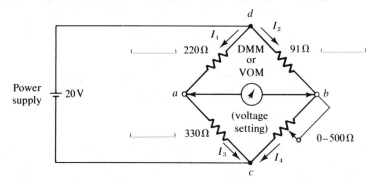

FIG. 13.3

(b) Starting with a higher voltage scale, vary the potentiometer until the voltage V_{ab} is as close to zero as possible. Then drop the voltage scales to the lowest range possible to set the voltage V_{ab} as close to zero volts as possible. The bridge is now balanced.

(c) Measure the following voltages:

$V_{da} = $ _____ , $V_{db} = $ _____

$V_{ac} = $ _____ , $V_{bc} = $ _____

(d) Calculate the currents I_1 and I_3 using Ohm's law. Are they equal as defined in the Résumé of Theory?

$$I_1 = \underline{\hspace{3cm}}, I_3 = \underline{\hspace{3cm}}$$

(e) Disconnect one lead of the potentiometer (used as a rheostat) and measure its resistance.

$$R_{pot} = \underline{\hspace{3cm}}$$

Calculate the currents I_2 and I_4 using the results of (d) and Ohm's law. Are they equal as defined in the Résumé of Theory?

$$I_2 = \underline{\hspace{3cm}}, I_4 = \underline{\hspace{3cm}}$$

(f) Verify that the following ratio is satisfied:

$$\frac{R_1}{R_3} = \frac{R_2}{R_4}$$

(g) Replace the 91-Ω resistor by the unknown resistor. Proceed as before to adjust the potentiometer until $V_{ab} \cong 0\,\text{V}$. Remove the variable resistor and measure its resistance with the ohmmeter section of your multimeter.

$$R_{pot} = \underline{\hspace{3cm}}$$

(h) Calculate $R_{unknown}$ using Eq. (13.3) from the Résumé of Theory.

$$R_x = \underline{\hspace{3cm}}$$

(i) What is the maximum value of resistance that this network could measure? Why?

$$R_{max} = \underline{\hspace{2in}}$$

Part 2 Commercial Wheatstone Bridge

(a) Use the commercial Wheatstone bridge to measure the resistance of the unknown resistor.

$R_x = \underline{\hspace{1.5in}}$

(b) Measure R_x using the ohmmeter section of your multimeter.

$R_x = \underline{\hspace{1.5in}}$

Compare with the results of (a) and Part 1(h).

Part 3 Δ-Y Conversions

(a) Construct the network of Fig. 13.4. Insert the measured values of each resistor.

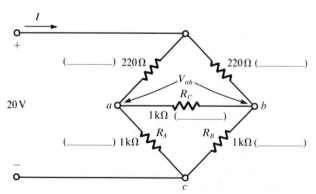

FIG. 13.4

(**b**) Calculate the current I and the voltage V_{ab} using any method. Use the measured resistor values.

$I =$ _____ , $V_{ab} =$ _____

(**c**) Measure the current I and the voltage V_{ab} and compare with the results of (b).

$I =$ _____ , $V_{ab} =$ _____

(**d**) Calculate the equivalent Y for the Δ formed by the three 1-kΩ resistors. Draw the equivalent circuit with the Δ replaced by the Y. Insert the values of the resistors in the Y in Fig. 13.5 and also indicate on the diagram those available fixed resistors that have a resistance level closest to calculated value.

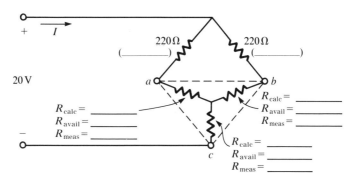

FIG. 13.5

(e) Construct the network drawn in (d) and measure the current I and voltage V_{ab}. Are they approximately the same as obtained in (c)? If so, why?

$I =$ _____ , $V_{ab} =$ _____

(f) Calculate I using the measured resistance values and compare to (c).

$I =$ _____

(g) Calculate the input resistance to the network of (d) using the measured resistor values.

R_T (calculated) = _____

(**h**) Disconnect the supply and measure the input resistance to the network of (d). Compare to the results of (g).

R_T (measured) = _____

(**i**) Determine the input resistance to the network of (a) using $R_T = E/I$ and compare to the results of (h). Should they compare? Why?

R_T = _____

OBJECT

To study the various types of circuits used in ohmmeters.

EQUIPMENT REQUIRED

Resistors (fixed)

1—1 kΩ, 22 kΩ

2—10 kΩ

Resistors (variable)

1—(0–10 kΩ) potentiometer

1—(0–250 kΩ) potentiometer

Instruments

1—DMM

1—dc Power supply 0–30 V, 0–0.5 A

1—0–1-mA, 1000-Ω meter movement

Ohmmeter Circuits

Experiment dc

14

EQUIPMENT ISSUED

TABLE 14.1

Item	Manufacturer and Model No.	Laboratory Serial No.
DMM		
Power Supply		

TABLE 14.2

Resistors	
Nominal Value	Measured Value
1 kΩ	
10 kΩ	
10 kΩ	
22 kΩ	

RÉSUMÉ OF THEORY

The ohmmeter is an instrument that is used to measure resistance. It is usually only 3% accurate. When resistance is to be measured more accurately, one must use such instruments as the Wheatstone bridge or the Kelvin bridge.

The majority of commerical ohmmeters fall into one of the following three categories:

1.   Series type, Fig. 14.1(a)
2.   Shunt type, Fig. 14.1(b)
3.   Voltage-divider type, Fig. 14.1(c)

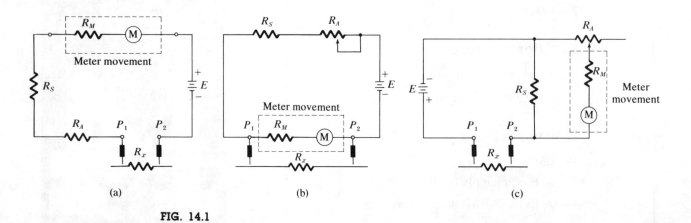

(a)   (b)   (c)

FIG. 14.1

The *series* type reads right to left. It cannot be used for low-resistance measurements (below 1 Ω).

The *shunt* type reads left to right. It is used primarily for low-resistance measurements (below 1000 Ω).

The *voltage-divider* type reads right to left. It is the most versatile and most often used.

In using an ohmmeter, one must remember two important rules:

1. Never leave the ohmmeter on or, in the case of a VOM, in the ohmmeter position. The voltage source is always in the circuit so that the life span of the battery is shortened.
2. Always adjust the "ohms adjustant" after changing the range.

PROCEDURE

Part 1   Series Ohmmeter Circuit

Construct the circuit of Fig. 14.2.

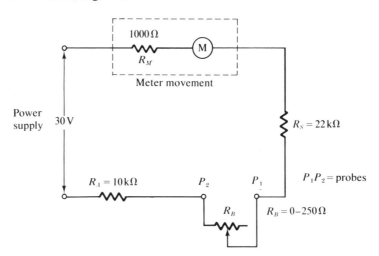

FIG. 14.2

Short the probes together and adjust the power supply until the meter reads 1 mA. Record in Table 14.3. Hold the probes apart and read the meter. Record in Table 14.3.

For the remaining steps of the experiment, proceed as follows:

Connect the 0–250-kΩ potentiometer across the probes. Use the DMM to set the potentiometer resistance to the values shown in Table 14.3. Disconnect one side each time and set the resistance. Then reconnect and read the meter (M). Record in Table 14.3. Plot the data of Table 14.3 using the divisions in Graph 14.1 for horizontal and vertical axes.

The graph is now used as a calibration chart for the ohmmeter circuit of Fig. 4.2. That is, for any unknown applied resistor, the resulting current will define an intersection with the plot of Graph 14.1 that will then define the resistance level on the horizontal axis.

TABLE 14.3

Resistance Across Probes	Meter Reading
0 kΩ	
30 kΩ	
60 kΩ	
90 kΩ	
120 kΩ	
150 kΩ	
180 kΩ	
210 kΩ	
240 kΩ	
Open Circuit	

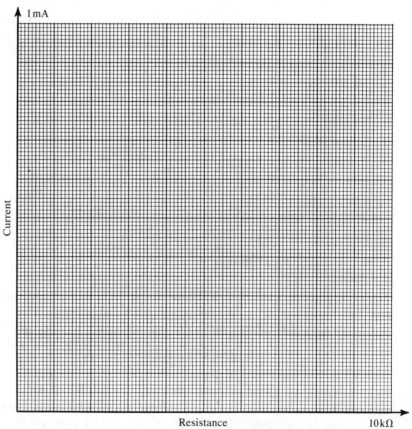

GRAPH 14.1

Vary the 0–250-kΩ potentiometer randomly for three settings and use your ohmmeter circuit to measure the resistance. In each case, use the DMM to verify the results.

$R_1 =$ _____ , $R_2 =$ _____ , $R_3 =$ _____

$R_{1(DMM)} =$ _____ , $R_{2(DMM)} =$ _____ ,

$R_{3(DMM)} =$ _____

Draw a meter scale for your ohmmeter.

Would the scale of this ohmmeter be considered linear or nonlinear?

What is the range of resistance values that this ohmmeter is capable of measuring with reasonably accurate results? Explain.

Why would you recommend that, for the greatest accuracy, the meter be read to the right of the center portion of the scale?

Part 2   Shunt Ohmmeter Circuit

Construct the circuit of Fig. 14.3.

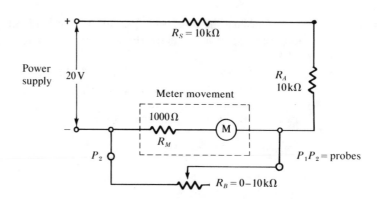

FIG. 14.3

Keeping the probes apart, adjust the power supply until the meter reads 1 mA. Record in Table 14.4. Short the probes together; then read the meter. Record in Table 14.4.

TABLE 14.4

Resistance Across Probes	Meter Reading
0 Ω	
200 Ω	
400 Ω	
800 Ω	
1,000 Ω	
2,000 Ω	
4,000 Ω	
6,000 Ω	
8,000 Ω	
10,000 Ω	

Connect the 0–10-kΩ potentiometer (R_B) across the probes. Use the DMM to set the potentiometer resistance to the values shown in Table 14.4. Remember to disconnect one side each time when setting the resistance. Reconnect and then read the meter. Record in Table 14.4. Plot the data of Table 14.4 using the horizontal and vertical divisions in Graph 14.2.

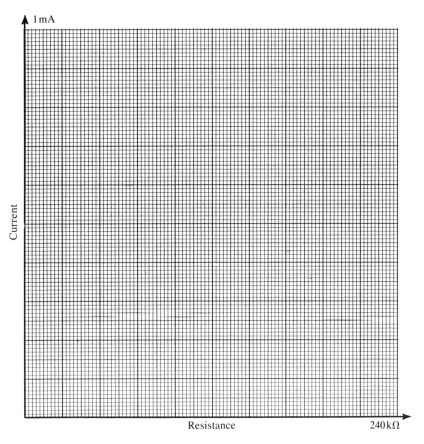

GRAPH 14.2

Graph 14.2 can now be used as a calibration chart for the shunt circuit of Fig. 14.3.

Now set the 0–10-kΩ potentiometer (R_B) to three random values and determine the resistance using the calibration curve. Check the results with the DMM.

$R_1 = $ _____ , $R_2 = $ _____ , $R_3 = $ _____

$R_{1(DMM)} = $ _____ , $R_{2(DMM)} = $ _____ ,

$R_{3(DMM)} = $ _____

How do the results compare?

Compare and contrast the two scales of the series and shunt ohmmeters. Comment accordingly.

Draw a meter scale for your ohmmeter.

Part 3   Voltage-Divider Ohmmeter

Construct the circuit of Fig. 14.4.

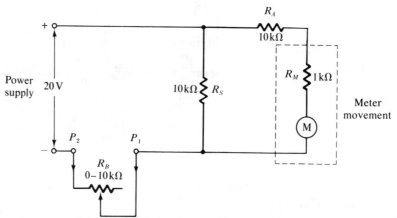

FIG. 14.4

Short the probes and adjust the power supply until the meter reads 1 mA. Record in Table 14.5. Separate the probes and again read the meter. Record in Table 14.5. Now connect the 0–10-kΩ potentiometer (R_B) across the probes. Use the DMM to set the potentiometer resistance to the values shown in Table 14.5. Disconnect one side each time and then set the resistance. Reconnect; then read the meter for each setting. Record in Table 14.5.

Plot the data of Table 14.5 using the vertical and horizontal divisions in Graph 14.3.

This graph can now be used as a calibration chart for the voltage-divider ohmmeter circuit of Fig. 14.4. Now set the 0–10-kΩ potentiometer (R_B) to three random values, reading the meter each time. Check the results with the DMM.

$R_1 =$ _____ , $R_2 =$ _____ , $R_3 =$ _____

$R_{1(DMM)} =$ _____ , $R_{2(DMM)} =$ _____ ,

$R_{3(DMM)} =$ _____

TABLE 14.5

Resistance Across Probes	Meter Reading
0 Ω	1 mA
500 Ω	
1,000 Ω	
2,000 Ω	
3,000 Ω	
4,000 Ω	
5,000 Ω	
8,000 Ω	
10,000 Ω	
∞	0

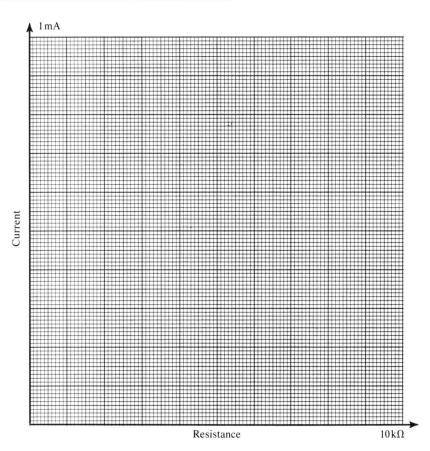

GRAPH 14.3

How do the results compare?

Draw a meter scale for your ohmmeter.

Summarize by comparing and contrasting the three circuits as to their advantages, disadvantages, and characteristics.

OBJECT

To measure voltages and currents with the oscilloscope.

EQUIPMENT REQUIRED

Resistors

1—100 Ω

1—(0–10 kΩ) potentiometer

Instruments

1—DMM

1—Oscilloscope

1—Audio oscillator

Miscellaneous

2—D batteries with holder

1—Single-pole, double-throw switch

The Oscilloscope as a Voltage and Current Measuring Instrument

Experiment ac

1

EQUIPMENT ISSUED

TABLE 1.1

Item	Manufacturer and Model No.	Laboratory Serial No.
DMM		
Oscilloscope		
Audio Oscillator		

TABLE 1.2

Resistors	
Nominal Value	Measured Value
100 Ω	

RÉSUMÉ OF THEORY

The cathode-ray oscilloscope is an instrument that allows us to see the variations of a voltage or current with time. The most important component of the oscilloscope is the cathode-ray tube (CRT), on whose screen the varying quantities are made visual. A typical CRT is shown schematically in Fig. 1.1.

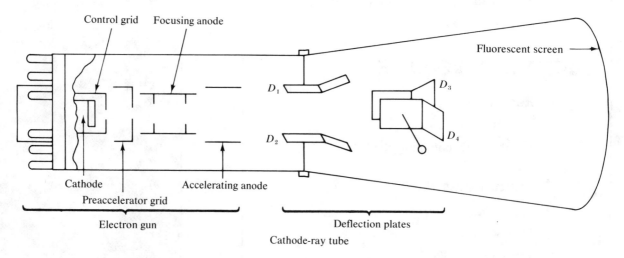

FIG. 1.1

The CRT is an evacuated glass envelope, shaped as shown in Fig. 1.1, which contains the following essential components:

   1.   An electron gun that produces rapidly moving electrons, shapes them into a pencil-like beam, and then directs them along the axis of the tube.

2. Deflection plates for producing a deflection of the beam from its original path.
3. A flourescent screen that emits light at the point where the beam strikes.

The electron gun is made up of the following components:

1. A heater and cathode that serve as the source of the electrons.
2. A control electrode that serves to vary the strength of the beam current.
3. A focusing electrode that focuses the beam to a sharp point on the screen.
4. Accelerating and preaccelerating electrodes that give the electrons the high velocity required to reach the screen and cause secondary emission.

The deflection of the beam may be accomplished either electrostatically or electromagnetically. Most oscilloscopes use electrostatic deflection (Fig. 1.1). To deflect the beam, a potential is applied across plates D_1 and D_2, or D_3 and D_4. The horizontal plates D_1 and D_2 deflect the beam vertically, whereas the vertical plates D_3 and D_4 deflect the beam horizontally. The deflection of the beam is directly proportional to the impressed voltage.

The CRT is, unfortunately, not a very sensitive device. A 5-inch CRT, under ordinary conditions, will give about 1 inch of deflection for a difference of potential of 100 V. The signals encountered most frequently are usually well under 100 V, so it becomes necessary to amplify the signals before a usable deflection will be obtained. Two deflection amplifiers are required, one for each set of plates.

For the oscilloscope to indicate the variations of an electrical quantity on the vertical as a function of time, there must be a voltage impressed on the horizontal deflection plates that varies linearly with time. This voltage is shown graphically in Fig. 1.2. An oscillator that can generate such a voltage is called, for obvious reasons, a *sawtooth oscillator*. Frequently, the term *sweep oscillator* is used. Fig. 1.3 shows a block diagram of a general-purpose oscilloscope.

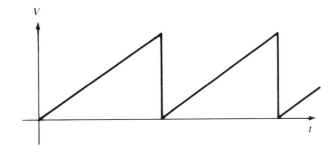

FIG. 1.2

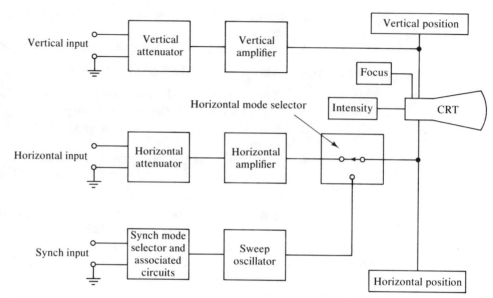

FIG. 1.3

All of the controls for the proper operation of an oscilloscope are mounted on the front panel of the instrument. Fig. 1.4 indicates the approximate location of the controls found on most general-purpose oscilloscopes. The location of the controls shown varies according to manufacturer.

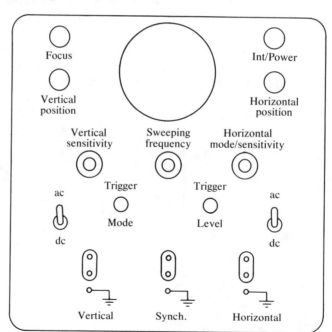

FIG. 1.4

Table 1.3 lists each control and its function.

TABLE 1.3

Control	Function
1. On-Off switch	Turns on the main power.
2. Intensity	Controls the intensity of the pattern on the screen.
3. Focus	Focuses the electron beam so that the pattern will be clearly defined.
4. Vertical position	Positions the pattern vertically.
5. Horizontal position	Positions the pattern horizontally.
6. Vertical sensitivity	Controls the voltage fed to the vertical amplifiers.
7. Horizontal sensitivity	Controls the voltage fed to the horizontal amplifiers.
8. ac-dc Switch for input	Puts a capacitor in series with the input terminals for ac and takes it out for dc.
9. Sweep frequency (time base)	Sets the sawtooth oscillator so that the beam will sweep across the screen at the proper rate.
10. Synch selector	Selects the various synchronization modes.
11. Positive or negative trigger and level	Determines whether triggering should take place on the positive or negative peak and at what level.

VOLTAGE MEASUREMENT

To use the oscilloscope as a voltage-measuring instrument, connect the unknown voltage to the vertical input terminals. Then measure the amount of vertical deflection of the electron beam and record. The magnitude of the unknown voltage can then be computed using the following relationship:

$$\text{Volts (unknown)} = \text{voltage sensitivity} \left(\frac{\text{volts}}{\text{div}}\right) \times \text{deflection (div)}$$

For example, if the beam is deflected a distance of 4.6 div as shown in Fig. 1.5, and the vertical sensitivity control is set to 0.01 V/div, then the impressed voltage can be found by

$$V_{(p\text{-}p)} = 0.01 \, \frac{V}{\text{div}} \times 4.6 \, \text{div} = 0.046 \, V = 46 \, mV$$

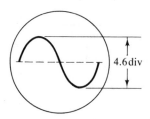

FIG. 1.5

CURRENT MEASUREMENT

Although primarily a voltage-measuring instrument, the oscilloscope can be used to measure current in the following way.

A small, known resistor (R_S) is inserted in series with the circuit in question so that the current (I) to be measured flows through R_S. The oscilloscope is then placed across R_S, and the voltage (V_R) is measured. Since $V_{R_S} = IR_S$, $I = V_{R_S}/R_S$. To avoid loading down the circuit (that is, changing the current to be measured), be sure that the value of R_S is much less than the total resistance (R_T) of the circuit through which I flows. A good rule of thumb is to keep R_S equal to or less than $R_T/100$ ($R_S \leq R_T/100$) so that loading effects can be ignored for most applications.

PROCEDURE

Part 1   Calibration of the Oscilloscope and Its Use as a Voltmeter

(a) Read the description of the controls in the manufacturer's instruction manual. Turn on the oscilloscope only after you have become familiar with the locations and functions of the controls. Now vary the controls indicated in Table 1.4 and record the observed effects.

TABLE 1.4

Control	Observed Effect
Focus	
Intensity	
Vertical Position	
Horizontal Position	

(b) Set up the circuit of Fig. 1.6. Set the vertical sensitivity of the oscilloscope to 1 V/div and the variable potentiometer to mid-range. Switch the vertical mode from ac to dc a few times and describe the effect. Explain why this effect takes place.

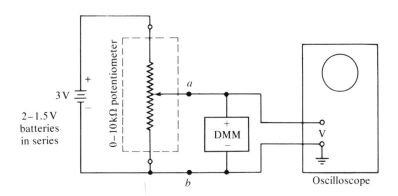

FIG. 1.6

With the vertical on dc mode, vary the output voltage from 0.4 V to 2.5 V as shown in Table 1.5 (setting the voltage V_{ab} with the DMM), each time recording the deflection of the oscilloscope trace. To get the most accurate values of deflection, you must vary the vertical sensitivity setting for each measurement.

TABLE 1.5

V_{ab} (dc)	Oscilloscope Deflection (cm)	Vertical Sensitivity (V/cm)	V_{ab} as Measured by Oscilloscope
0.4 V			
1.0 V			
2.5 V			

How can you locate the zero line on the oscilloscope screen? Describe the procedure.

(c) Construct the network of Fig. 1.7.

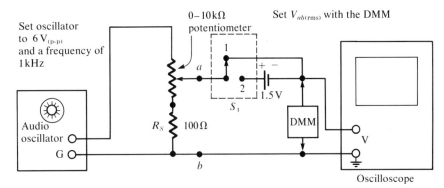

FIG. 1.7

Set the horizontal mode to internal and the vertical mode to dc, and connect the oscilloscope as indicated in Fig. 1.7. Place S_1 in position #1. Vary the voltage V_{ab} using the potentiometer, as indicated in Table 1.6, and record the deflection on the oscilloscope trace. Vary the horizontal sweep frequency control until at least two cycles are shown on the screen.

TABLE 1.6

$V_{ab(rms)}$ DMM Reading	$V_{ab(p\text{-}p)}$ $(2\sqrt{2})[V_{ab(rms)}]$	Oscilloscope Vertical Deflection	Vertical Sensitivity Setting (V/cm)	$V_{ab(p\text{-}p)}$ as Measured by the Oscilloscope
0.177 V				
0.354 V				
0.531 V				
2.122 V				

(d) Adjust the vertical sensitivity to 1 V/div. Vary the potentiometer until a 4-div peak-to-peak trace is on the oscilloscope screen. See Fig. 1.8.

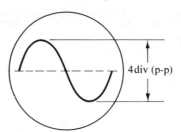

4 div (p-p)

FIG. 1.8

Center the trace vertically and horizontally. Switch S_1 is still in position #1. Now change the vertical mode to ac and observe the effect. Explain why there was no change in the trace.

Place S_1 in position #2 and again switch from ac to dc mode. Explain the effect.

How much deflection was there of the zero line of the ac wave, with respect to the oscilloscope zero line?

Zero line displacement = _____

Calculate the voltage necessary to cause this displacement.

$$V_{dc} = \underline{\hspace{3cm}}$$

How does this value compare to the 1.5-V dc of the battery?

Part 2   Current Measurement

Construct the circuit of Fig. 1.9.

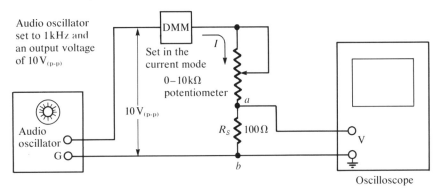

FIG. 1.9

Vary the 0–10-kΩ potentiometer so that the current I in the circuit changes from 0.4 mA to 1.0 mA in four steps, as indicated in Table 1.7. For each setting, record the deflection of the oscilloscope trace and the vertical sensitivity setting. The voltage V_{ab} and the current I can be calculated using the relationships

$$V_{ab(p\text{-}p)} = (V/div) \times (div)$$

$$V_{ab(max)} = \frac{V_{ab(p\text{-}p)}}{2}$$

$$V_{ab(rms)} = 0.707\, V_{ab(max)}$$

$$I_{(rms)} = \frac{V_{ab(rms)}}{R_S} \text{ (use the measured value of } R_S)$$

TABLE 1.7

Milliammeter Setting ($I_{(rms)}$)	Oscilloscope Deflection	V/cm Vertical Sensitivity	V_{ab}		$I_{(rms)} = \dfrac{V_{ab(rms)}}{R_S}$
			(p-p)	(rms)	
0.4 mA					
0.6 mA					
0.8 mA					
1.0 mA					

Summarize your conclusions.

OBJECT

To measure the impedance of a resistor, inductor, and capacitor at a fixed frequency.

EQUIPMENT REQUIRED

Resistors

1—10 Ω, 100 Ω, 1.2 kΩ, 3.3 kΩ

Inductors

2—5 H (fixed or decade)

Capacitors

2—1 μF

Instruments

1—DMM

1—Oscilloscope

1—Audio oscillator

EQUIPMENT ISSUED

TABLE 2.1

Item	Manufacturer and Model No.	Laboratory Serial No.
DMM		
Oscilloscope		
Oscillator		

TABLE 2.2

Resistors	
Nominal Value	Measured Value
$10\,\Omega$	
$100\,\Omega$	
$1.2\,k\Omega$	
$3.3\,k\Omega$	

RÉSUMÉ OF THEORY

For impedances in series, the total impedance is the sum of the individual impedances:

$$\boxed{\mathbf{Z}_T = \mathbf{Z}_1 + \mathbf{Z}_2 + \mathbf{Z}_3 + \cdots + \mathbf{Z}_n} \tag{2.1}$$

For resistors in series,

$$R_T = R_1 + R_2 + R_3 + \cdots + R_n \tag{2.2}$$

which is independent of frequency.

For inductors in series,

$$X_{LT} = X_1 + X_2 + X_3 + \cdots + X_n$$
$$= 2\pi f L_1 + 2\pi f L_2 + 2\pi f L_3 + \cdots + 2\pi f L_n = 2\pi f L_T$$

and

$$\boxed{L_T = L_1 + L_2 + L_3 + \cdots + L_n} \tag{2.3}$$

Note that the individual and total inductive reactances are directly proportional to frequency.

For capacitors in series,

$$X_{C_T} = X_1 + X_2 + X_3 + \cdots + X_n$$
$$= \frac{1}{2\pi f C_1} + \frac{1}{2\pi f C_2} + \frac{1}{2\pi f C_3} + \cdots + \frac{1}{2\pi f C_n} = \frac{1}{2\pi f C_T}$$

where

$$\frac{1}{C_T} = \frac{1}{C_1} + \frac{1}{C_2} + \frac{1}{C_3} + \cdots + \frac{1}{C_n}$$ (2.4)

Note that the individual and total capacitive reactance are inversely proportional to frequency. Consider the special case of only two capacitors in series:

$$X_{C_T} = \frac{1}{2\pi f C_T} \qquad \text{where} \qquad C_T = \frac{C_1 C_2}{C_1 + C_2}$$

For resistors in parallel,

$$\frac{1}{R_T} = \frac{1}{R_1} + \frac{1}{R_2} + \frac{1}{R_3} + \cdots + \frac{1}{R_n}$$ (2.5)

which is independent of frequency.

For inductors in parallel,

$$\frac{1}{X_{L_T}} = \frac{1}{X_1} + \frac{1}{X_2} + \frac{1}{X_3} + \cdots + \frac{1}{X_n} = \frac{1}{2\pi f L_1} + \frac{1}{2\pi f L_2} + \frac{1}{2\pi f L_3} + \cdots + \frac{1}{2\pi f L_n}$$

$$= \frac{1}{2\pi f L_T}$$

where

$$\frac{1}{L_T} = \frac{1}{L_1} + \frac{1}{L_2} + \frac{1}{L_3} + \cdots + \frac{1}{L_n}$$ (2.6)

Consider the special case of only two inductors in parallel:

$$X_{L_T} = \frac{X_1 X_2}{X_1 + X_2} = 2\pi f L_T$$

where

$$X_1 = 2\pi f L_1, \qquad X_2 = 2\pi f L_2 \qquad \text{and} \qquad L_T = \frac{L_1 L_2}{L_1 + L_2}$$

For capacitors in parallel,

$$\frac{1}{X_{C_T}} = \frac{1}{X_1} + \frac{1}{X_2} + \frac{1}{X_3} + \cdots + \frac{1}{X_n} = 2\pi f C_1 + 2\pi f C_2 + 2\pi f C_3 + \cdots + 2\pi f C_n = 2\pi f C_T$$

where

$$C_T = C_1 + C_2 + C_3 + \cdots + C_n$$ (2.7)

Consider the special case of only two capacitors in parallel:

$$X_{C_T} = \frac{X_1 X_2}{X_1 + X_2} = \frac{1}{2\pi f C_T}$$

where

$$C_T = C_1 + C_2$$

PROCEDURE

Part 1   Resistance

(a) Construct the circuit of Fig. 2.1. Insert the actual values of the resistors as determined by the ohmmeter section of your multimeter.

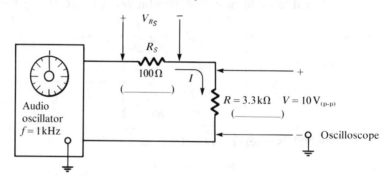

FIG. 2.1

Caution: Always ensure that the ground of the oscilloscope is connected to the ground of the oscillator. Otherwise a hazardous situation may result.

(b) Set the voltage across R to $10\,V_{(p\text{-}p)}$ using the oscilloscope. Then turn off the oscillator and oscilloscope and reverse the positions of R_S and R by interchanging the leads to the oscillator. This last maneuver will ensure that the grounds of the oscilloscope and oscillator are in common when the next measurement is made. Measure the voltage across the sensing resistor with the oscilloscope.

$$V_{R_{S(p\text{-}p)}} = \underline{\hspace{3cm}}$$

(c) Calculate the current through the series circuit from

$$I_{(p\text{-}p)} = \frac{V_{R_{S(p\text{-}p)}}}{R_S}$$

$$I_{(p\text{-}p)} = \underline{\hspace{3cm}}$$

(d) Determine the resistance R from

$$R = \frac{V_{(p\text{-}p)}}{I_{(p\text{-}p)}}$$

and compare to the ohmmeter measured value.

$$R = \underline{\hspace{3cm}}, \quad R_{(\text{ohmmeter})} = \underline{\hspace{3cm}}$$

(e) Connect a 1.2-kΩ and 3.3-kΩ resistor in series in place of the resistor R. Using the measured resistor values, calculate the total resistance R_T.

R_T (calculated) = _____

(f) Set the voltage across the series combination to 10 V$_{(p-p)}$ using the oscillo-scope, and then measure the voltage $V_{R_S(p-p)}$ after reversing the positions of R_S and the series combination of resistors. Calculate the current $I_{(p-p)}$.

$V_{R_S(p-p)}$ = _____ , $I_{(p-p)}$ = _____

(g) Calculate the resistance R_T from your readings and compare to the results of (e).

R_T (measured) = _____ , R_T [Part 1 (e)] = _____

(h) Connect the 1.2-kΩ and 3.3-kΩ resistors in parallel in place of the resistor R of Fig. 2.1. Using the measured values of each resistor, calculate the total resistance R_T.

R_T (calculated) = _____

(i) Set the voltage across the parallel combination to $10\,V_{(p\text{-}p)}$ using the oscilloscope, and then measure the voltage $V_{R_{S(p\text{-}p)}}$ after reversing the positions of R_S and the parallel combination of resistors. Calculate the current $I_{(p\text{-}p)}$.

$$V_{R_{S(p\text{-}p)}} = \rule{3cm}{0.4pt} \, , \ I_{(p\text{-}p)} = \rule{3cm}{0.4pt} .$$

(j) Calculate the resistance R_T from your readings and compare to the results of (h).

$$R_T \text{ (measured)} = \rule{3cm}{0.4pt} \, , \ R_T \text{ [Part 1 (h)]} = \rule{3cm}{0.4pt}$$

Part 2   Capacitive Reactance

(a) Construct the network of Fig. 2.2. Insert the measured resistor value for R_S.

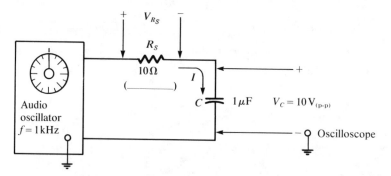

FIG. 2.2

(b) Set the voltage V_C to $10\,V_{(p\text{-}p)}$ and measure the voltage $V_{R_{S(p\text{-}p)}}$ after reversing the positions of the capacitor and sensing resistor. Calculate the current $I_{(p\text{-}p)}$.

$$V_{R_{S(p\text{-}p)}} = \rule{3cm}{0.4pt} \, , \ I_{(p\text{-}p)} = \rule{3cm}{0.4pt}$$

(c) Calculate the reactance X_C from the measurements of (b).

$$X_C \text{ (measured)} = \rule{3cm}{0.4pt}$$

(**d**) Calculate the reactance using the applied frequency and capacitor nameplate value. Compare to the results of (c).

X_C (calculated) = _____

(**e**) Connect two capacitors in series (each $1\,\mu\text{F}$) in place of C in Fig. 2.2 and set V_C to $10\,\text{V}_{(\text{p-p})}$. Then record the value of $V_{R_{S(\text{p-p})}}$ after reversing the positions of the resistor and series capacitors. Calculate the value of $I_{(\text{p-p})}$.

$V_{R_{S(\text{p-p})}}$ = _____ , $I_{(\text{p-p})}$ = _____

(**f**) Using the results of (e), calculate the value of X_{C_T}.

X_{C_T} (measured) = _____

(**g**) Calculate the total reactance using the applied frequency and the capacitor nameplate values. Compare to the results of (f).

X_{C_T} (calculated) = _____ , X_{C_T} [Part 2 (f)] = _____

(**h**) Connect two capacitors in parallel (each $1\,\mu\text{F}$) in place of C in Fig. 2.2 and set V_C to $10\,\text{V}_{(\text{p-p})}$. Then record the value of $V_{R_{S(\text{p-p})}}$ after reversing the positions of the resistor and parallel capacitors. Calculate the value of $I_{(\text{p-p})}$.

$V_{R_{S(\text{p-p})}}$ = _____ , $I_{(\text{p-p})}$ = _____

(i) Using the results of (h), calculate the value of X_{C_T}.

X_{C_T} (measured) = _____

(j) Calculate the total reactance using the applied frequency and the capacitor nameplate values. Compare to the results of (i).

X_{C_T} (calculated) = _____ , X_{C_T} [Part 2 (i)] = _____

Part 3   Inductive Reactance

(a) Construct the network of Fig. 2.3. Insert the measured values for R_S and R_l.

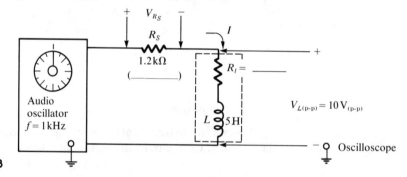

FIG. 2.3

(b) Set the voltage V_L to 10 V$_{(p-p)}$ and measure the voltage $V_{R_{S(p-p)}}$ after reversing the positions of the resistor R_S and the inductor. Calculate the current $I_{(p-p)}$.

$V_{R_{S(p-p)}}$ = _____ , $I_{(p-p)}$ = _____

(c) Calculate the reactance X_L from the measurements of (b). Ignore the effects of R_l.

X_L (measured) = _____

(d) Calculate the reactance using the applied frequency and the inductor nameplate value. Compare to the results of (c).

X_L (calculated) = _____

(e) Connect two inductors in series (each 5 H) in place of L in Fig. 2.3 and set V_L to 10 V$_{(p-p)}$. Then record the value of $V_{R_{S(p-p)}}$ after reversing the positions of R_S and the series combination of inductors. Calculate the value of $I_{(p-p)}$.

$V_{R_{S(p-p)}}$ = _____ , $I_{(p-p)}$ = _____

(f) Using the results of (e), calculate the value of X_{L_T}. Ignore the effects of R_l.

X_{L_T} (measured) = _____

(g) Calculate the total reactance using the applied frequency and the inductor nameplate values. Compare to the results of (f).

X_{L_T} (calculated) = _____ , X_{L_T} (f) = _____

(h) Connect two inductors in parallel (each 5 H) in place of L in Fig. 2.3 and set V_L to 10 V$_{(p-p)}$. Then record the value of $V_{R_{S(p-p)}}$ after reversing the positions of R_S and the parallel combination of inductors. Calculate the value of $I_{(p-p)}$.

$V_{R_{S(p-p)}}$ = _____ , $I_{(p-p)}$ = _____

(i) Using the results of (h), calculate the value of X_{L_T}. Ignore the effects of R_l.

X_{L_T} (measured) = _____

(j) Calculate the total reactance using the applied frequency and the inductor nameplate values. Compare to the results of (i).

X_{L_T} (calculated) = _____ , X_{L_T} [Part 3 (i)] = _____

OBJECT

To note the effect of frequency on the basic R-L-C components.

EQUIPMENT REQUIRED

Resistors

1—1 kΩ

Inductors

1—5 H

Capacitors

1—0.1 μF

Instruments

1—DMM

1—Oscilloscope

1—Audio oscillator

Frequency Dependence of R-L-C Components

Experiment ac

3

EQUIPMENT ISSUED

TABLE 3.1

Item	Manufacturer and Model No.	Laboratory Serial No.
DMM		
Oscilloscope		
Audio Oscillator		

TABLE 3.2

Resistors	
Nominal Value	Measured Value
1 kΩ	

RÉSUMÉ OF THEORY

The resistance of a carbon resistor is unaffected by frequency, except for extremely high frequencies. This rule is also true for the total resistance of resistors in series or parallel.

The reactance of an inductor is linearly dependent on the frequency applied. That is, if we double the frequency, we double the reactance, as determined by $X_L = 2\pi fL$. For very low frequencies, the reactance is correspondingly very small, while for increasing frequencies, the reactance will increase to a very large value. For dc conditions, we find that $X_L = 2\pi(0)L$ is zero ohms, corresponding with the short-circuit representation we used in our analysis of dc circuits. For very high frequencies, X_L is so high that we can often use an open-circuit approximation.

The capacitor behaves (as far as reactance is concerned) in a manner opposite to that of the inductor. For low frequencies, the capacitive reactance, as determined by $X_C = 1/2\pi fC$ is very high and approaches the open-circuit approximation used for dc circuits. For very high frequencies, the reactance gets progressively smaller until the short-circuit approximation could be employed. The capacitive reactance is also linearly dependent on the frequency.

PROCEDURE

Part 1   Resistors

Construct the circuit of Fig. 3.1. Insert the measured value of R.

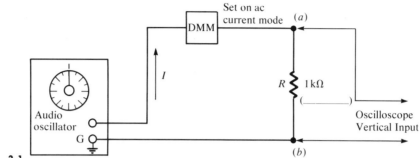

FIG. 3.1

In this part of the experiment, the voltage across the resistor will be held constant while varying only the frequency. If the resistance is frequency dependent, the current through the circuit should also change as a function of frequency. Therefore, by maintaining the voltage V_{ab} constant and changing the frequency while monitoring the current I, we can verify if, indeed, resistance is frequency independent.

Set the voltage V_{ab} to 3 $V_{(p-p)}$ (measure this voltage with the oscilloscope). Then set the frequencies to those shown in Table 3.3, each time monitoring V_{ab} (always 3 $V_{(p-p)}$) and I. Since we are using the DMM for current measurement, this value is given in rms. Record the values in Table 3.3.

TABLE 3.3

Frequency (Hz)	$V_{ab(p\text{-}p)}$	$V_{ab(rms)}$	$I_{(rms)}$	$R = V_{ab(rms)}/I_{(rms)}$
100	3 V			
200	3 V			
500	3 V			
1,000	3 V			
2,000	3 V			

Does the current in the circuit change as a function of frequency? If not, why?

Part 2 Inductors

(a) Construct the circuit of Fig. 3.2. (Measure the dc resistance of the coil with the DMM and record that value as R_l on the diagram.)

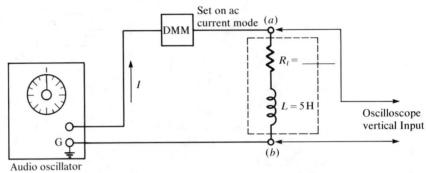

FIG. 3.2   Audio oscillator

In this part, the resistor of Part 1 is replaced by the inductor. Here again, the voltage across the inductor will be maintained constant while varying the frequency of that voltage and monitoring the current in the circuit.

Set the voltage V_{ab} to 15 $V_{(p-p)}$ (use the oscilloscope to measure V_{ab}) and the oscillator to the various frequencies shown in Table 3.4, each time making sure that $V_{ab} = 15 V_{(p-p)}$ and that you measure the current I (remember I will be in rms). Record in Table 3.4.

TABLE 3.4

Frequency (Hz)	$V_{ab(p-p)}$	$V_{ab(rms)}$	$I_{(rms)}$	$Z = V_{ab(rms)}/I_{(rms)}$	$X_L = \sqrt{(Z)^2 - (R_l)^2}$
100	15 V				
200	15 V				
500	15 V				
1,000	15 V				
2,000	15 V				

(b) Calculate $V_{ab(rms)} = V_{ab(p-p)}/2\sqrt{2}$ for each frequency and record in Table 3.4.

(c) Calculate the total impedance Z (magnitude only) at each frequency and insert the values in Table 3.4.

(d) For each frequency, determine X_L from $X_L = \sqrt{Z^2 - R_l^2}$ and insert the values in Table 3.4.

(e) Plot the reactance X_L versus frequency on Graph 3.1. Is it a linear (straight-line) curve? Discuss your results.

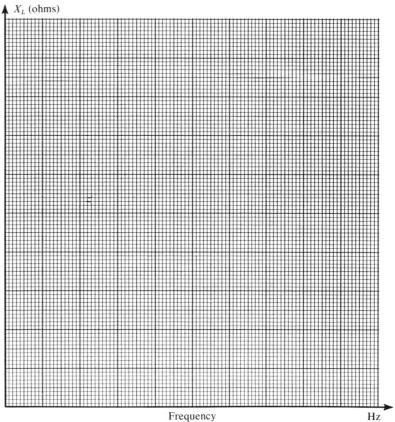

GRAPH 3.1   Frequency   Hz

(f) Determine the inductance at 1500 Hz using the results of (e). Compare to the nameplate value.

L (calculated) = _____ , L (nameplate) = _____

Part 3   Capacitors

(a) Construct the circuit of Fig. 3.3. This part is exactly the same as Part 2 except that we now insert a capacitor in place of the inductor.

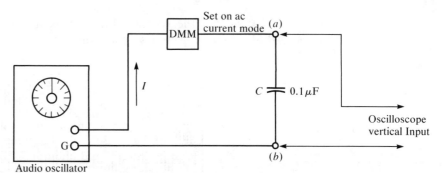

FIG. 3.3   Audio oscillator

Set the voltage V_{ab} to 5 $V_{(p\text{-}p)}$ (use the oscilloscope to measure V_{ab}) and the oscillator to the various frequencies shown in Table 3.5. Make sure that $V_{ab} = 5\ V_{(p\text{-}p)}$ and that you measure the current I (I will be in rms) for each setting. Record in Table 3.5.

TABLE 3.5

Frequency (Hz)	$V_{ab(p\text{-}p)}$	$V_{ab(rms)}$	$I_{(rms)}$	$X_C = V_{ab(rms)}/I_{(rms)}$
100	5 V			
200	5 V			
500	5 V			
1,000	5 V			
2,000	5 V			

(b) Calculate $V_{ab(rms)} = V_{ab(p\text{-}p)}/2\sqrt{2}$ for each frequency. Record in Table 3.5.

(c) Calculate the reactance X_C at each frequency and insert the values in Table 3.5.

(d) Plot the reactance X_C versus frequency on Graph 3.2. Is it a linear (straight-line) curve? Discuss your results.

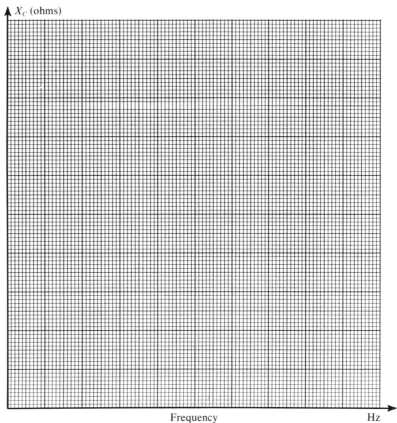

X_C (ohms)

GRAPH 3.2

Frequency   Hz

(e) Determine the reactance of the capacitor at 1500 Hz from the plot and calculate the capacitance of the capacitor. Compare to the nameplate value.

C (calculated) = _____ , C (nameplate) = _____

OBJECT

To plot the frequency response of the R-L, R-C *networks.*

EQUIPMENT REQUIRED

Resistors

1—1 kΩ, 6.8 kΩ

Inductors

1—5 H

Capacitors

2—0.1 μF

Instruments

1—DMM

1—Oscilloscope

1—Audio oscillator

EQUIPMENT ISSUED

TABLE 4.1

Item	Manufacturer and Model No.	Laboratory Serial No.
DMM		
Oscilloscope		
Audio Oscillator		

TABLE 4.2

Resistors	
Nominal Value	Measured Value
1 kΩ	
6.8 kΩ	

RÉSUMÉ OF THEORY

For the series dc or ac circuit, the voltage drop across a particular element is directly related to its impedance as compared to the other series elements. Since the impedance of the inductor and capacitor will change with frequency, the voltage across both elements will be determined by the applied frequency.

For the series R-L network, the voltage across the coil will increase with frequency since the inductive reactance increases directly with frequency and the impedance of the resistor is essentially independent of the applied frequency (in the audio range).

For the series R-C network, the voltage will decrease with increasing frequencies since the capacitive reactance is inversely proportional to the applied frequency.

Since the voltage and current of the resistor are related by the fixed resistance value, the shape of their curves versus frequency will be the same.

Keep in mind that the voltages across the elements in an ac circuit are vectorially related. Otherwise, the voltage readings may appear to be totally incorrect and not satisfy Kirchhoff's voltage law.

Caution: **Be sure that all measurements are made with the oscilloscope and oscillator sharing a common ground. The elements of the network may have to be reversed as occurred in Experiment 2.**

PROCEDURE

Part 1   R-L Network

(a) Construct the network of Fig. 4.1. Insert the measured value of the resistors R and R_l on the diagram.

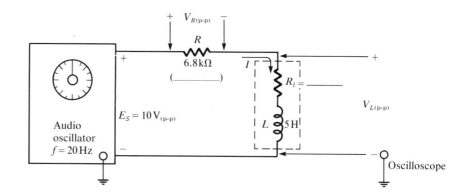

FIG. 4.1

(b) Maintaining $10\,V_{(p-p)}$ at the input to the circuit, record the voltages $V_{L(p-p)}$ and $V_{R(p-p)}$ for the frequencies indicated in Table 4.3. Calculate the level of $I_{(p-p)}$ from $I_{(p-p)} = V_{R(p-p)}/R$ and complete the table.

TABLE 4.3

Frequency (Hz)	$V_{L(p-p)}$	$V_{R(p-p)}$	$I_{(p-p)}$
20			
50			
100			
150			
200			
250			
300			
500			
700			
1,000			

(c) Sketch the curves of $V_{L(\text{p-p})}$ and $V_{R(\text{p-p})}$ versus frequency on Graph 4.1.

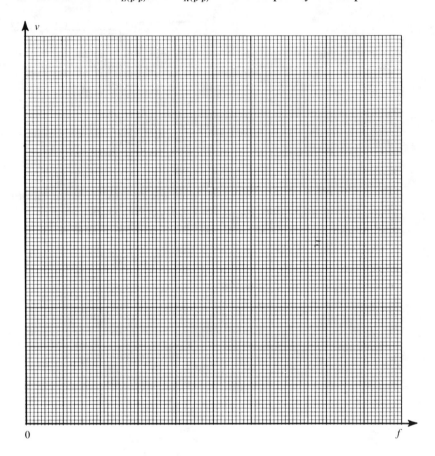

GRAPH 4.1

(d) At 100 Hz, does the magnitude of $V_{L(\text{p-p})} + V_{R(\text{p-p})} = E_{S(\text{p-p})}$? Comment accordingly. How are they related?

(e) Sketch the curve of $I_{(\text{p-p})}$ versus frequency on Graph 4.2. How does it compare to the graph of $V_{R(\text{p-p})}$ versus frequency?

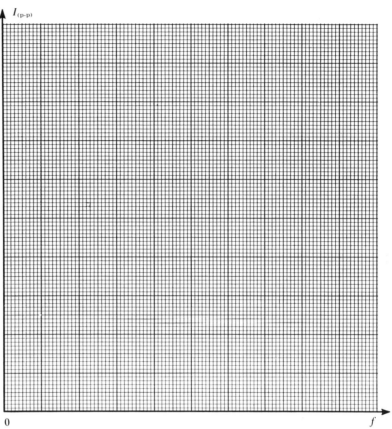

GRAPH 4.2

 (f) At a frequency of 100 Hz, calculate the reactance of the inductor using $X_L = 2\pi fL$. Compare to the value obtained from the data of Table 4.3 using

$$Z = V_{L(p\text{-}p)}/I_{(p\text{-}p)} \quad \text{and} \quad X_L = \sqrt{Z^2 - R_l^2}$$

X_L (calculated) = _____ , X_L (from data) = _____

(g) Determine, using vector algebra, the voltage $V_{L(p\text{-}p)}$ at a frequency of 100 Hz and compare to the results appearing in Table 4.3. Include the effects of R_l.

$V_{L(p\text{-}p)}$ (calculated) = _____ , $V_{L(p\text{-}p)}$ (measured) = _____

(h) At low frequencies the inductor approaches a low-impedance short-circuit equivalent and at high frequencies a high-impedance open-circuit equivalent. Does the data of Table 4.3 and Graphs 4.1 and 4.2 verify the above statement? Comment accordingly.

Part 2   R-C Network

(a) Construct the network of Fig. 4.2. Insert the measured value of the resistor R.

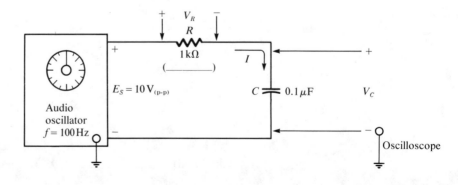

FIG. 4.2

(b) Maintaining 10 V$_{(p-p)}$ at the input to the circuit, record the voltages $V_{C(p-p)}$ and $V_{R(p-p)}$ for the frequencies indicated in Table 4.4. Calculate the level of $I_{(p-p)}$ from $I_{(p-p)} = V_{R(p-p)}/R$ and complete the table.

TABLE 4.4

Frequency (Hz)	$V_{C(p-p)}$	$V_{R(p-p)}$	$I_{(p-p)}$
100			
200			
400			
500			
1,000			
3,000			
5,000			
7,000			
10,000			
20,000			

(c) Sketch the curves of $V_{C(p-p)}$ and $V_{R(p-p)}$ versus frequency on Graph 4.3.

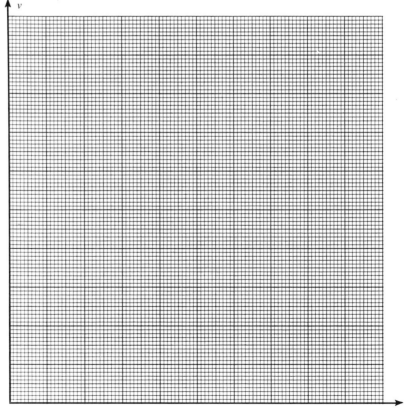

GRAPH 4.3   0 f

(d) At 500 Hz, does the magnitude of $V_{L(\text{p-p})} + V_{R(\text{p-p})} = E_{S(\text{p-p})}$? Comment accordingly. How are they related?

(e) Sketch the curve of $I_{(\text{p-p})}$ versus frequency on Graph 4.4. How does it compare to the graph of $V_{R(\text{p-p})}$ versus frequency?

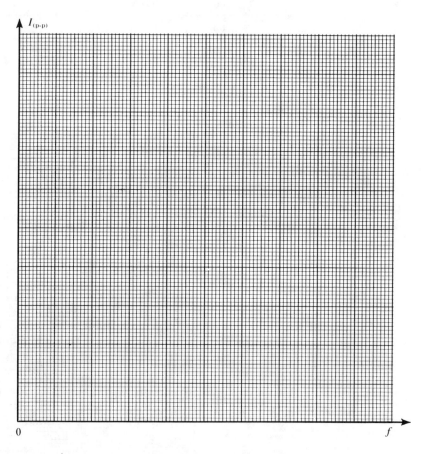

GRAPH 4.4   0 f

(f) At a frequency of 500 Hz, calculate the reactance of the capacitor using $X_C = 1/2\pi f C$. Compare to the value obtained from the data of Table 4.4 using

$$X_C = \frac{V_{C(\text{p-p})}}{I_{(\text{p-p})}}$$

X_C (calculated) = _____ , X_C (from data) = _____

(g) Determine, using vector algebra, the voltage $V_{C(p\text{-}p)}$ at a frequency of 100 Hz and compare to the results appearing in Table 4.4.

$V_{C(p\text{-}p)}$ (calculated) = _____ , $V_{C(p\text{-}p)}$ (measured) = _____

(h) At low frequencies the capacitor approached a high-impedance open-circuit equivalent and at high frequencies a low-impedance short-circuit equivalent. Does the data of Table 4.4 and Graphs 4.3 and 4.4 verify the above statement? Comment accordingly.

(i) Connect two $0.1\,\mu$F capacitors in parallel and plot the graph of $V_{C(p-p)}$ versus frequency on Graph 4.3. Are the results what you expected? Why? Use the same values for E_S and R.

The Oscilloscope in Frequency and Phase Measurements

Experiment
ac

5

OBJECT

To use the oscilloscope in the measurement of frequency and phase.

EQUIPMENT REQUIRED

Resistors

1—1 kΩ, 18 kΩ

1—(0–10 kΩ) potentiometer

Capacitors

1—0.5 μF

Instruments

1—DMM

1—Oscilloscope

1—Audio oscillator

Miscellaneous

Transformer, 120-V primary, 12.6-V secondary

EQUIPMENT ISSUED

TABLE 5.1

Item	Manufacturer and Model No.	Laboratory Serial No.
DMM		
Oscilloscope		
Audio Oscillator		

TABLE 5.2

Resistors	
Nominal Value	**Measured Value**
1 kΩ	
18 kΩ	

RÉSUMÉ OF THEORY

The two ways of measuring frequency with the oscilloscope are

    1. Using the calibrated time-base circuit built into the oscilloscope
    2. Using a known frequency and Lissajous patterns

In the following paragraphs, we will discuss each of the above methods.

THE CALIBRATED TIME-BASE METHOD

The horizontal sweep or time-base circuits of an oscilloscope generate a voltage that varies linearly with time and is called a sawtooth voltage. See Fig. 5.1. This voltage, when impressed across the horizontal deflection plates, causes the beam to be deflected from left to right. Since the voltage increases at a rate proportional to time, the beam is also deflected at a rate proportional to time. That is, for any specified period of time (millisecond, microsecond, second) that elapses, the beam will have traveled a specific distance.

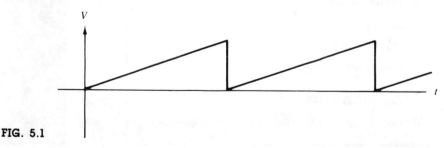

FIG. 5.1

For example, if the oscilloscope screen is divided into ten equal divisions, the beam might be caused to move at a rate of 0.5 s per division, 0.05 s per division, or 10 ms per division. The rate is usually variable and can be set by a control labeled sweep time or time base. This sweep feature allows us to measure the frequency of any alternating or varying voltage.

Let us consider a certain alternating voltage (sinusoidal) of an unknown frequency, which causes the trace shown in Fig. 5.2 when applied to the vertical input of an oscilloscope. Notice that the complete cycle covers a distance of 8 divisions. Since we know the time it takes the beam to traverse one division, we can calculate the period and then the frequency. We know the time by merely noting the setting of the horizontal sweep control. Let us assume that the setting is 0.01 s per division (s/div). Then we can obtain the period (T) by multiplying the number of divisions for one cycle by the dial setting. Finally, we take the reciprocal of T for the frequency (f):

$$\text{Dial setting} = 0.01 \text{ s/div} \times 8 \text{ div/cycle} = 0.08 \text{ s/cycle}$$

$$f = \frac{1}{0.08 \text{ s/cycle}} = 12.5 \text{ cycles/s} = 12.5 \text{ Hz}$$

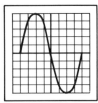

FIG. 5.2

The above demonstrates the use of the oscilloscope as a frequency-measuring instrument.

THE KNOWN-FREQUENCY AND LISSAJOUS-PATTERN METHOD

When the oscilloscope does not have a calibrated sweep, then the Lissajous-pattern approach is used. This method makes use of certain patterns that are generated when two sinusoids are simultaneously applied to the oscilloscope—one at the vertical input and the other at the horizontal input. One of the applied signals must have a known frequency so that the other signal can then be calculated. Let us outline the procedure, analyze it, and then finally calculate the frequency of an unknown signal. The steps of the procedure are as follows:

1. Connect the unknown signal to the vertical input.
2. Connect the known-frequency signal to the horizontal input and set the horizontal mode control to external.
3. Set both vertical and horizontal sensitivities so that the two signals give equal deflection.
4. Apply both signals simultaneously.
5. Take note of the pattern and analyze as follows.

Assume that the trace is as shown in Fig. 5.3. Further, assume that the known frequency is 1000 Hz. We will label the frequency of the signal at vertical f_V and that at the horizontal f_H.

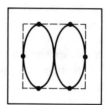

FIG. 5.3

Since the known is at the horizontal, $f_H = 1000$ Hz. There is a relationship that exists between the ratio of the two frequencies and the tangencies or points of contact of the curves to the vertical and horizontal axes. This relationship is

$$\frac{f_V}{f_H} = \frac{H_T}{V_T}$$

where

f_V = frequency of the signal at the vertical input

f_H = frequency of the signal at the horizontal input

H_T = number of tangencies on the horizontal axis

V_T = number of tangencies on the vertical axis

For the trace of Fig. 5.3,

$$f_H = 1000\,\text{Hz} \qquad H_T = 2 \qquad V_T = 1$$

Therefore,

$$\frac{f_V}{1000} = \frac{2}{1} \qquad \text{so that } f_V = 2000\,\text{Hz}$$

Let us consider one more example. With a known frequency of 9000 Hz on the horizontal input and an unknown frequency on the vertical, the pattern shown in Fig. 5.4 appears on the oscilloscope screen. Find the frequency of the vertical signal. The pattern shows the following:

$$H_T = 1 \qquad V_T = 3 \qquad f_H = 9000\,\text{Hz}$$

$$\frac{f_V}{9000} = \frac{1}{3} \qquad \text{Therefore, } f_V = \frac{9000}{3} = 3000\,\text{Hz}$$

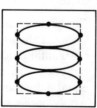

FIG. 5.4

The above demonstrates that the oscilloscope can be used for frequency measurements in the absence of a calibrated sweep.

PHASE MEASUREMENTS

When two signals of the same frequency are to be compared as to phase, the oscilloscope can again be used very effectively. There are two methods available.

1. Dual-trace comparison with the calibrated time base
2. Lissajous pattern

DUAL-TRACE METHOD OF PHASE MEASUREMENT

The dual-trace method of phase measurement, aside from providing a higher degree of accuracy, can more easily compare two signals of different amplitude and, in fact, different wave shape. The method can be applied directly to oscilloscopes equipped with two vertical channels or to a conventional single-trace oscilloscope with an external electronic switch. See Fig. 5.5.

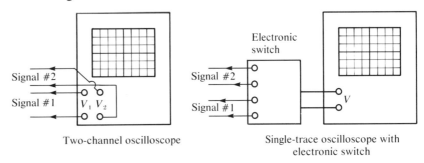

FIG. 5.5

Two-channel oscilloscope   Single-trace oscilloscope with electronic switch

Regardless of which oscilloscope is available, the procedure essentially consists of displaying both traces on the screen simultaneously, and measuring the distance (in scale divisions) between two identical points on the two traces.

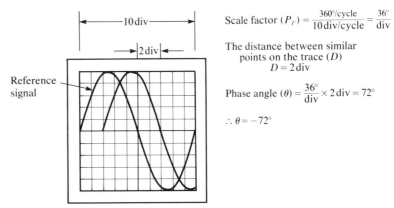

Scale factor $(P_F) = \dfrac{360°/\text{cycle}}{10\,\text{div/cycle}} = \dfrac{36°}{\text{div}}$

The distance between similar points on the trace (D)
$$D = 2\,\text{div}$$

Phase angle $(\theta) = \dfrac{36°}{\text{div}} \times 2\,\text{div} = 72°$

$\therefore \theta = -72°$

FIG. 5.6

One signal will act as a reference, that is, zero-phase angle. Normally the signal introduced at the channel being used as trigger will be considered the reference. On some oscilloscopes one can trigger from either channel. In the comparison, therefore, we can assume that the signal being compared is leading $(+\theta)$ if it is to the left of the reference and lagging $(-\theta)$ if it is to the right of the reference. To use the dual-trace phase-measurement method, therefore, proceed as follows:

1. Connect the two signals to the two vertical channels making sure to observe proper grounding and to connect the signal to be used as reference to the channel used for triggering.
2. Select the mode of operation—"Alternate" or "Chop." For frequencies less than 50 kHz, use "Chop." For frequencies greater than 50 kHz, use "Alternate."
3. Once the traces are on the screen, adjust the vertical sensitivities so that the two traces are approximately the same size.
4. Adjust the sweep control until one cycle (if possible) of the reference signal occupies 10 divisions horizontally. This will always give you a scale factor $P_F = 36°/\text{div}$.

Now measure the distance between the two identical points on the zero axis and compute the phase angle (θ), using the expression

Phase angle (θ) = [scale factor (P_F)] × [distance measured (D)]

If the signal being compared crosses the zero axis before the reference, it is a positive phase angle $(+\theta)$. If it crosses after the reference signal, it is a negative phase angle $(-\theta)$.

Note the example appearing in Fig. 5.6

LISSAJOUS-PATTERN PHASE MEASUREMENT

This method is also called the *X-Y* phase measurement. To use this method proceed as follows:

1. Connect the two signals to the vertical and the horizontal inputs, respectively.
2. A pattern known as a *Lissajous* will appear on the screen. The type of pattern will indicate certain common-phase relationships, and in fact, the patterns can be used to calculate the phase angle in general.

The patterns shown in Fig. 5.7 indicate the phase relationship appearing with each figure.

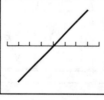 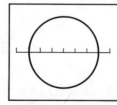 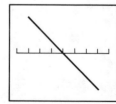

FIG. 5.7 $\theta = 0°$ or $360°$ $\theta = 90°$ or $270°$ $\theta = 180°$

The patterns shown in Fig. 5.8 can be used to calculate the phase angle (θ) as indicated below the figures.

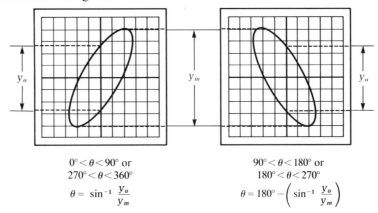

$0° < \theta < 90°$ or
$270° < \theta < 360°$

$\theta = \sin^{-1} \dfrac{y_o}{y_m}$

$90° < \theta < 180°$ or
$180° < \theta < 270°$

$\theta = 180° - \left(\sin^{-1} \dfrac{y_o}{y_m} \right)$

FIG. 5.8

Example: Assume that the patterns in Figs. 5.9 and 5.10 appear on an oscilloscope screen. Calculate the phase angle θ in each case.

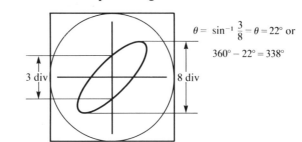

$\theta = \sin^{-1} \dfrac{3}{8} = \theta = 22°$ or

$360° - 22° = 338°$

3 div   8 div

FIG. 5.9

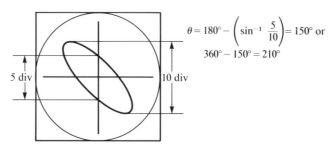

$\theta = 180° - \left(\sin^{-1} \dfrac{5}{10} \right) = 150°$ or

$360° - 150° = 210°$

5 div   10 div

FIG. 5.10

PROCEDURE

Part 1   Measuring Frequency with the Calibrated Time Base

(a) Connect the output of the audio oscillator to the vertical input of the oscilloscope. See Fig. 5.11. Set the oscilloscope horizontal mode to internal and the audio oscillator to 2000 Hz. Adjust the oscillator attenuator and the oscilloscope vertical sensitivity so that the signal is 8 divisions peak-to-peak. Vary the time base control (sweep control) until the length of one cycle can be accurately measured. Record the dial setting and the cycle length in Table 5.3. Now vary the frequency in 2000-Hz steps as indicated in the table, each time recording the dial setting and the cycle length. Finally, fill in the remaining columns.

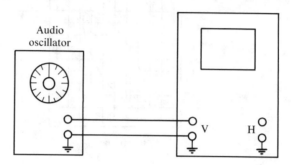

FIG. 5.11

TABLE 5.3

A Oscillator Dial Setting	B Oscilloscope Dial Setting (Horizontal Sensitivity)	C Length of One Cycle	T Period of One Cycle (T = B × C)	f Frequency $\left(f = \frac{1}{T}\right)$
2,000 Hz				
4,000 Hz				
6,000 Hz				
8,000 Hz				
10,000 Hz				
12,000 Hz				
14,000 Hz				
16,000 Hz				
18,000 Hz				
20,000 Hz				

Frequency Measurement with Lissajous Patterns

(b) Connect the 12.6 V transformer to the horizontal input of the oscilloscope as shown in Fig. 5.12. Set the horizontal mode to internal. Connect the audio oscillator to the vertical input and use the oscilloscope to set V_V to 10 V peak-to-peak at 60 Hz.

The 60 Hz from the transformer is being used as the known frequency. Vary the frequency of the oscillator (below 1000 Hz) until the patterns shown in Table 5.4 appear. Each time, calculate the frequency and compare to the dial reading of the oscillator. Due to the nonlinearities of the transformer, the waveshapes may not look exactly as shown.

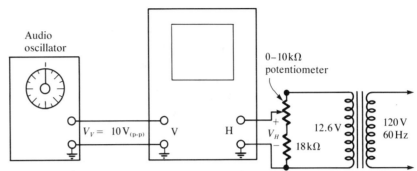

FIG. 5.12   Adjust the $0-10\,\mathrm{k\Omega}$ potentiometer until the voltage V_H is $10\,\mathrm{V_{(p\text{-}p)}}$.

TABLE 5.4

Lissajous Pattern	Calculation		Calculated Frequency (Hz)	Dial Osc. Setting (Hz)
	$f_H - 60\,\mathrm{Hz}$	$H_T =$ _____	$f_V =$ _____	
		$V_T =$ _____		
	$f_H = 60\,\mathrm{Hz}$	$H_T =$ _____	$f_V =$ _____	
		$V_T =$ _____		
	$f_H = 60\,\mathrm{Hz}$	$H_T =$ _____	$f_V =$ _____	
		$V_T =$ _____		
	$f_H = 60\,\mathrm{Hz}$	$H_T =$ _____	$f_V =$ _____	
		$V_T =$ _____		

Part 2 Dual-Trace Phase Measurement

(a) Construct the circuit of Fig. 5.13.

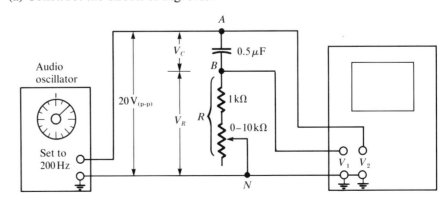

FIG. 5.13

Set the oscillator output to a maximum of $20\,V_{(p\text{-}p)}$. Now vary the potentiometer as shown in Table 5.5. Check the resistance each time by removing it and measuring with the DMM. Each time the resistance is set to the value given in Table 5.5, measure the amplitude of V_{AN}, V_{BN}, and the phase angle between them. Since the angle associated with V_{AN} in Table 5.5 is zero degrees, the phase angle measured is θ_1 in Table 5.5. The columns for R, X_C, V_{AN}, and V_R can now be completed for each setting. Use effective values for the voltages V_{AN}, V_R and V_C.

TABLE 5.5

Potentiometer Setting	R	X_C	$V_{AN} \angle 0°$	(Fig. 5.13) $V_R = V_{BN} \angle \theta_1$	(Fig. 5.14) $V_C = V_{BN} \angle \theta_2$
0			$\angle 0°$		
$2{,}000\,\Omega$			$\angle 0°$		
$4{,}000\,\Omega$			$\angle 0°$		

(b) Now interchange the position of the capacitor and the two resistors. See Fig. 5.14. Keep the same oscillator output. The potentiometer is again set to the values shown in Table 5.5, but now we are measuring V_{AN}, V_{BN} and the phase angle θ_2. Note that the voltage V_{AN} is the same as before, but now V_{BN} is the voltage across the capacitor so that θ_2 can be determined.

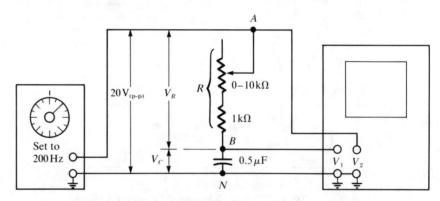

FIG. 5.14

(c) Draw the phasor diagram for V_{AN}, V_R and V_C for each of the potentiometer settings. Use the coordinates given on Graph 5.1. Label all voltages.

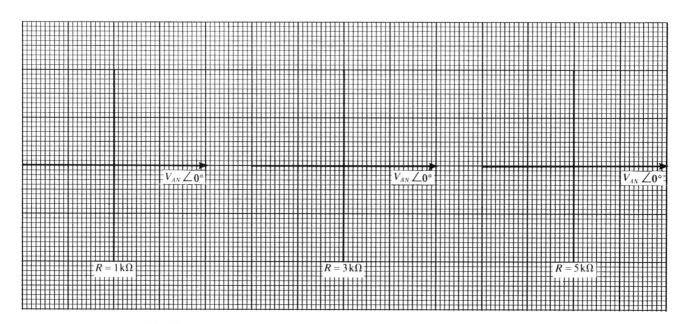

GRAPH 5.1

(d) What is the phase relationship between the voltages V_C and V_R according to theory and the above phasor diagrams?

Part 3   Phase Measurement with Lissajous Patterns

(a) Connect the oscilloscope to the circuit shown in Fig. 5.15.

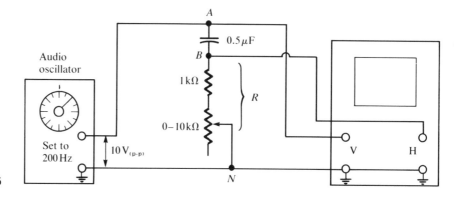

FIG. 5.15

Set the potentiometer to the three values indicated in Table 5.6, each time measuring the y-intercept (y_o) and the y-maximum (y_m), and recording these values. Calculate the phase angle θ and fill in the remaining columns of the table.

TABLE 5.6

Potentiometer Setting	R	y_o	y_m	θ_1	$V_R = V_{BN} \underline{/\theta_1}$
0					
2,000 Ω					
4,000 Ω					

(b) How do the values of θ_1, measured this way, compare to those obtained in Part 2(a)?

(c) Repeat the above for θ_2 making the necessary circuit modifications and creating your own table of values. Compare to the results of Part 2(b).

OBJECT

To investigate the behavior of series sinusoidal ac circuits at a frequency of 1 kHz.

EQUIPMENT REQUIRED

Resistors
1—18 kΩ

Inductors
1—5 H

Capacitors
1—0.01 μF

Instruments
1—DMM
1—Oscilloscope
1—Audio oscillator

Series Sinusoidal Circuits

Experiment
ac

6

EQUIPMENT ISSUED

TABLE 6.1

Item	Manufacturer and Model No.	Laboratory Serial No.
DMM		
Oscilloscope		
Audio Oscillator		

TABLE 6.2

Resistors	
Nominal Value	**Measured Value**
18 kΩ	

RÉSUMÉ OF THEORY

Kirchhoff's voltage law is applicable to ac circuits, but it is now stated as follows: *The phasor sum of the voltages around a closed loop is equal to zero.*

For example, in a series circuit, the source voltage is the phasor sum of the component (load) voltages. For a series R-L-C circuit,

$$E^2 = V_R{}^2 + (V_L - V_C)^2$$

so that

$$\boxed{E = \sqrt{V_R{}^2 + (V_L - V_C)^2}} \tag{6.1}$$

where

E = source voltage

V_R = voltage across the total resistance of the circuit

V_L = voltage across the total inductance

V_C = voltage across the total capacitance

Since the resistance and the reactance of a series R-L-C circuit are in quadrature,

$$Z^2 = R^2 + X_T{}^2 \qquad \text{where } X_T \text{ (total reactance)} = X_L - X_C \tag{6.2}$$

In a series R-L-C sinusoidal circuit, the voltage across a reactive component may be greater than the input voltage.

The average power (in watts) delivered to a sinusoidal circuit is

$$\boxed{P = I^2 R = VI \cos \theta} \tag{6.3}$$

where the values of the current and the voltage are the effective values.
The power factor F_p is given by

$$F_p = \frac{R_T}{Z_T} = \cos \theta \qquad (6.4)$$

where θ is the angle associated with the total impedance Z_T.

For an ideal inductor, the current lags the voltage across it by 90°. For a capacitor, the current leads the voltage across it by 90°. Inductive circuits are therefore called *lagging power factor circuits*, and capacitive circuits are called *leading power factor circuits*.

In a purely resistive circuit, the voltage and the current are inphase and the power factor is unity.

PROCEDURE

Part 1   Series R-L Circuit

(a) Construct the network of Fig. 6.1(a). Insert the measured value of R and R_l.

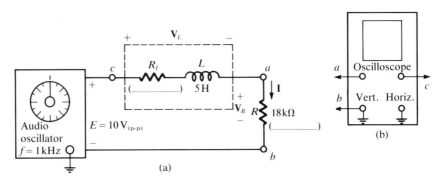

FIG. 6.1   (a)

(b) After setting E to $10\,V_{(p\text{-}p)}$, measure the voltages $V_{R(p\text{-}p)}$ and $V_{L(p\text{-}p)}$ with the oscilloscope. Be sure to reverse the positions of R and L before measuring V_L to ensure that the oscillator and the oscilloscope have a common ground.

$V_{R(p\text{-}p)} = $ _____ , $V_{L(p\text{-}p)} = $ _____

(c) Determine $I_{(p\text{-}p)}$ from $I_{(p\text{-}p)} = V_{R(p\text{-}p)}/R_{(meas)}$

$I_{(p\text{-}p)} = $ _____

(d) Determine the input impedance from $Z_T = E_{(p\text{-}p)}/I_{(p\text{-}p)}$. Ignore the effects of R_l since $R \gg R_l$ and $X_L \gg R_l$ at $f = 1000\,\text{Hz}$. In other words, consider the coil to be purely ideal at this frequency ($R_l \cong 0\,\Omega$).

$$Z_T = \underline{\hspace{3cm}}$$

(e) Calculate the total impedance (magnitude and angle) and current $I_{(p-p)}$ from the nameplate value of the coil and the measured resistance value. Ignore the effect of R_l.

$$\mathbf{Z}_T \text{ (theoretical)} = \underline{\hspace{3cm}} , \; I_{(p-p)} \text{ (calculated)} = \underline{\hspace{3cm}}$$

(f) Compare the results of (d) and (e) and explain the source of any differences.

(g) Show that your measurements from (b) satisfy Kirchhoff's voltage law. That is, demonstrate with vector addition that

$$\mathbf{E} = \mathbf{V}_R + \mathbf{V}_L$$

(h) Reduce the input voltage to zero and connect the oscilloscope to the points shown in Fig. 6.1(b). The oscilloscope controls should be set as follows:

1. Intensity and focus controls set to give a clear and visible trace.
2. Vertical and horizontal positioning controls set to center the trace on the screen.
3. Horizontal selector switch set to external horizontal.
4. Vertical and horizontal sensitivity controls set to the same position.

Consult the instructor regarding the setting of these controls since your particular oscilloscope may be labeled differently. Now adjust the voltage control until you get a pattern on the screen similar to that shown in Fig. 6.2. The phase angle between the horizontal and vertical deflection voltages can be computed by

$$\theta = \sin^{-1}\left(\frac{y_{\text{int}}}{y_m}\right) \qquad (6.5)$$

The Lissajous pattern on the oscilloscope will take any of the forms shown in Fig. 6.3, depending on the phase angle. The patterns shown are for equal-amplitude, equal-frequency sinusoids on both deflection systems.

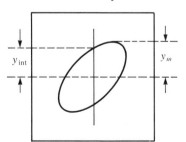

FIG. 6.2

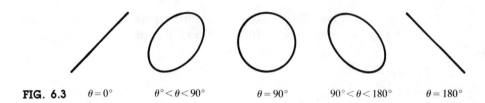

FIG. 6.3 $\theta = 0°$ $\theta° < \theta < 90°$ $\theta = 90°$ $90° < \theta < 180°$ $\theta = 180°$

Measure the quantities y_m and y_{int} on the oscilloscope screen and compute θ_T, the phase angle between the input voltage ($V_{cb} = E$), and the voltage across the resistor ($V_{ab} = V_R$). θ_T is also the angle between E and I and the angle of Z_T.

$\theta_T = $ _____

(i) Interchange the positions of the resistor and the coil, and repeat (h). The phase angle is now between the input voltage ($V_{cb} = E$) and the voltage across the coil ($V_{ab} = V_L$).

$\theta = $ _____

(j) Using the theoretical results of the previous parts, draw to scale the phasor diagram of all of the voltages and the current, with the current as the reference phasor. From this diagram, measure the angle between the input voltage and the resistor voltage, and compare it to the value from (h). Measure the angle between the input voltage and the coil voltage, and compare it to the value from (i).

θ_T [Part 1(h)] = _____ , θ_T (calculated) = _____
θ [Part 1(i)] = _____ , θ (calculated) = _____

(k) Perform the remaining calculations required to complete Table 6.3.

TABLE 6.3

	Measured or Calculated from Measured Values	Theoretical (calculated)
$E_{(p\text{-}p)}$		
$V_{R(p\text{-}p)}$		
$V_{L(p\text{-}p)}$		
$I_{(p\text{-}p)}$		
$E_{(rms)}$		
$V_{R(rms)}$		
$V_{L(rms)}$		
$I_{(rms)}$		
Z_T		
θ_T		
P_T		
F_p		

Part 2 Series R-C Circuit

(a) Construct the network of Fig. 6.4(a). Insert the measured resistor value.

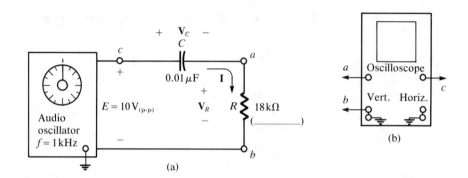

FIG. 6.4   (a)

(b) After setting E to $10\,V_{(p\text{-}p)}$, measure the voltages $V_{R(p\text{-}p)}$ and $V_{C(p\text{-}p)}$ with the oscilloscope. Be sure to reverse the positions of R and C before measuring V_C to ensure that the oscillator and the oscilloscope have a common ground.

$V_{R(p\text{-}p)} =$ _____ , $V_{C(p\text{-}p)} =$ _____

(c) Determine $I_{(p\text{-}p)}$ from $I_{(p\text{-}p)} = V_{R(p\text{-}p)}/R_{(meas)}$.

$I_{(p\text{-}p)} =$ _____

(d) Determine the input impedance from $Z_T = E_{(p\text{-}p)}/I_{(p\text{-}p)}$.

Z_T (measured) = _____

(e) Calculate the total impedance (magnitude and angle) and current $I_{(p\text{-}p)}$ from the nameplate value of the capacitance and the measured resistor value.

$\mathbf{Z}_T$ (theoretical) = _____ , $I_{(p\text{-}p)}$ (calculated) = _____

(f) Compare the results of (d) and (e) and explain the source of any differences.

(g) Show that your measurements from (b) satisfy Kirchhoff's voltage law. That is, demonstrate with vector addition that $\mathbf{E} = \mathbf{V}_R + \mathbf{V}_C$.

(h) Determine θ_T and θ (angle between the input voltage and the voltage across the capacitor) using Fig. 6.4(b) and the procedure outlined in the previous part.

$\theta_T =$ _____ , $\theta =$ _____

(i) Repeat Part 1(j) (replacing coil with capacitor as appropriate).

θ_T [Part 2(h)] = _____ , θ_T (calculated) = _____

θ [Part 2(h)] = _____ , θ (calculated) = _____

Perform the remaining calculations required to complete Table 6.4.

TABLE 6.4

	Measured or Calculated from Measured Values	Theoretical (calculated)
$E_{(p-p)}$		
$V_{R(p-p)}$		
$V_{C(p-p)}$		
$I_{(p-p)}$		
$E_{(rms)}$		
$V_{R(rms)}$		
$V_{C(rms)}$		
$I_{(rms)}$		
Z_T		
θ_T		
P_T		
F_p		

Part 3 R-L-C Network

(a) Construct the network of Fig. 6.5. Insert the measured resistance values. Ignore the effects of R_l in the following analysis.

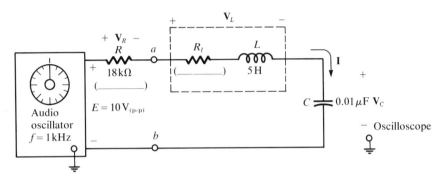

FIG. 6.5

(b) Measure all the component voltages with $E = 10\,\text{V}_{(p\text{-}p)}$. In order to ensure a common ground between the oscilloscope and oscillator for each measurement, be sure the element is placed in the position of the capacitor C. In other words, reverse the order of the elements so that the element across which the voltage is to be measured has the position of C indicated in Fig. 6.5.

$V_{R(p\text{-}p)} =$ _____ , $V_{L(p\text{-}p)} =$ _____ , $V_{C(p\text{-}p)} =$ _____

(c) Determine $I_{(p\text{-}p)}$ from $I_{(p\text{-}p)} = V_{R(p\text{-}p)}/R_{(meas)}$.

$I_{(p\text{-}p)} =$ _____

(d) Calculate Z_T from $Z_T = E_{(p\text{-}p)}/I_{(p\text{-}p)}$.

$Z_T =$ _____

(e) Using the nameplate values calculate Z_T and compare to the results of (d).

Z_T (calculated) = _____

(f) Verify Kirchhoff's law by showing that $\mathbf{E} = \mathbf{V}_R + \mathbf{V}_L + \mathbf{V}_C$. Show the phasor diagram.

(g) Use the voltage divider rule to determine the voltage $V_{ab(\text{p-p})}$.

$V_{ab(\text{p-p})}$ (calculated) = _____

(h) Measure the voltage V_{ab} and compare with the results of (g).

$V_{ab(\text{p-p})}$ (measured) = _____

OBJECT

To investigate the behavior of parallel sinusoidal ac circuits.

EQUIPMENT REQUIRED

Resistors

1—18 kΩ

3—100 Ω

Inductors

1—5 H

Capacitors

1—0.01 μF

Instruments

1—DMM

1—Oscilloscope

1—Audio oscillator

Parallel Sinusoidal Circuits

Experiment
ac

7

EQUIPMENT ISSUED

TABLE 7.1

Item	Manufacturer and Model No.	Laboratory Serial No.
DMM		
Oscilloscope		
Audio Oscillator		

TABLE 7.2

Resistors	
Nominal Value	Measured Value
18 kΩ	
100 Ω	
100 Ω	
100 Ω	

RÉSUMÉ OF THEORY

Kirchhoff's current law as applied to ac circuits states that the phasor sum of the currents entering and leaving a node must equal zero. For example, in a parallel circuit, the source current is the phasor sum of the component (load) currents. For a parallel R-L-C circuit, the magnitude of the source current I is given by $I = \sqrt{I_R^2 + I_{X_T}^2}$ where $I_{X_T} = I_{X_L} - I_{X_C}$ and I_{X_L} = current in the inductive branch, I_{X_C} = current in the capacitive branch, and I_R = current in the resistive branch.

In a parallel R-L-C circuit, it is possible for the magnitude of the source current I to be less than that of one of the branch currents.

Impedances in parallel combine according to the following equation:

$$\frac{1}{\mathbf{Z}_T} = \frac{1}{\mathbf{Z}_1} + \frac{1}{\mathbf{Z}_2} + \frac{1}{\mathbf{Z}_3} \qquad (7.1)$$

For two impedances in parallel, it is usually more convenient to use the equation in the form

$$\mathbf{Z}_T = \frac{\mathbf{Z}_1 \mathbf{Z}_2}{\mathbf{Z}_1 + \mathbf{Z}_2} \qquad (7.2)$$

In parallel R-L-C circuits, it is possible for the total impedance to be larger than the individual branch impedances.

In order to obtain the waveform of a current on an oscilloscope, it is necessary to send this current through a resistor and view the voltage across the resistor.

Since the voltage and current of a resistor are related by $\mathbf{E} = \mathbf{IR}$ (a linear relationship), the current and voltage waveforms are always of the same appearance and in phase.

PROCEDURE

Part 1   R-L Parallel Network

(a) Construct the network of Fig. 7.1. Insert the measured values of each resistor. The magnitude of R and X_L at the applied frequency permits ignoring (on an approximate basis) the effects of the two sensing resistors, R_{S_1} and R_{S_2}, and R_l when we analyze the system. In other words, assume you have an ideal parallel R-L system.

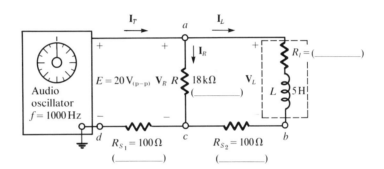

FIG. 7.1

(b) Using the nameplate inductor value (5 H) and the measured resistance level for R, calculate the various currents of the network.

$$I_{T(\text{p-p})} = \underline{\hspace{2cm}} , \ I_{R(\text{p-p})} = \underline{\hspace{2cm}} , \ I_{L(\text{p-p})} = \underline{\hspace{2cm}}$$

Calculate the rms values of the above quantities and insert below.

$$I_{T(\text{rms})} = \underline{\hspace{3cm}} , I_{R(\text{rms})} = \underline{\hspace{3cm}} , I_{L(\text{rms})} = \underline{\hspace{3cm}}$$

(c) Energize the network of Fig. 7.1 and set the input voltage to $20\,V_{(\text{p-p})}$ using the oscilloscope. Use the oscilloscope to measure the voltage $V_{R_{S_1}}$, and insert below.

$$V_{R_{S_1(\text{p-p})}} = \underline{\hspace{3cm}}$$

(d) In order to ensure that the oscilloscope and oscillator have a common ground, remove R_{S_1} and connect point c to point d. Measure the voltages

$$V_{R_{S_2(\text{p-p})}} = \underline{\hspace{3cm}} , V_{R(\text{p-p})} = \underline{\hspace{3cm}}$$

(e) Using the results of (c) and (d), calculate the peak-to-peak values of the various currents of the network using Ohm's law.

$$I_{T(\text{p-p})} = \underline{\hspace{3cm}} , I_{R(\text{p-p})} = \underline{\hspace{3cm}} , I_{L(\text{p-p})} = \underline{\hspace{3cm}}$$

(f) Calculate the rms values of the measured quantities and insert below. Compare to the results of (b).

$$I_{T(\text{rms})} = \underline{\hspace{3cm}} , I_{R(\text{rms})} = \underline{\hspace{3cm}} , I_{L(\text{rms})} = \underline{\hspace{3cm}}$$

(g) Is the total current I_T larger in magnitude than each branch current? Should it be?

(h) Using the input voltage as a reference ($\mathbf{E} = E \angle 0°$), and the measured rms values of the currents I_L and I_R, draw a phasor diagram to scale and measure the current I. How does it compare to the measured value? From the phasor diagram, determine the angle θ_T between I_T and I_R (same as between E and I_T), the angle θ between I_T and I_L, and the angle θ_1 between I_L and I_R.

I_T (diagram) = _____ , I_T (measured) = _____

θ_T = _____ , θ = _____ , θ_1 = _____

(i) Connect the oscilloscope as shown in Fig. 7.2. Do not reintroduce the resistor R_{S_1}. It will permit a measurement of the phase angle between the two branch currents I_R and I_L. Record the value of θ_1. Points a, b, and c appear on Fig. 7.1.

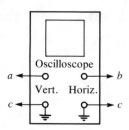

FIG. 7.2

θ_1 (measured) = _____ , θ_1 [Part 1 (h)] = _____

(j) Reintroduce the resistor R_{S_1} and connect the oscilloscope as shown in Fig. 7.3. The phase angle obtained will be between the input voltage E and the current I_T, or between I_R and I_T since E and I_R are in phase.

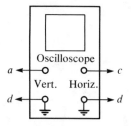

FIG. 7.3

θ_T (measured) = _____ , θ_T [Part 1(h)] = _____

(k) Using the fact that $\theta_T + \theta + \theta_1 = 180°$ for the right triangle of (g), find the measured value of θ using the measured values of (i) and (j). Compare to the results of (h).

θ (measured) = _____ , θ [Part 1(h)] = _____

Part 2 R-C Parallel Network

(a) Construct the network of Fig. 7.4. Insert the measured values of the resistors. As with the previous part, ignore the magnitude of R_{S_1} and R_{S_2} as compared to the other impedances of the network when making your calculations.

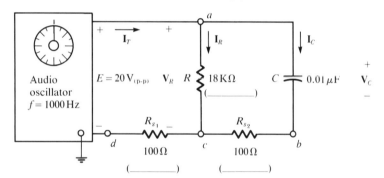

FIG. 7.4

(b) Using the nameplate capacitor value (0.01 μF) and the measured resistance level for R, calculate the various currents indicated below.

$I_{T(\text{p-p})}$ = _____ , $I_{R(\text{p-p})}$ = _____ , $I_{C(\text{p-p})}$ = _____

Calculate the rms values of the above quantities and insert below.

$I_{T(rms)} =$ _____ , $I_{R(rms)} =$ _____ , $I_{C(rms)} =$ _____

(c) Energize the network of Fig. 7.4 and set the input voltage to $20\,V_{(p-p)}$ using the oscilloscope. Use the oscilloscope to measure the voltage $V_{R_{S_1}}$ and insert below.

$V_{R_{S_{1(p-p)}}} =$ _____

Calculate the rms value of $V_{R_{S_1}}$.

$V_{R_{S_{1(rms)}}} =$ _____

(d) In order to ensure that the oscilloscope and oscillator have a common ground, remove R_{S_1} and connect point c to point d. Measure the voltages $V_{R_{S_2}}$ and V_R.

$V_{R_{S_{2(p-p)}}} =$ _____ , $V_{R(p-p)} =$ _____

Calculate the rms values of $V_{R_{S_2}}$ and V_R.

$V_{R_{S_{2(rms)}}} =$ _____ , $V_{R(rms)} =$ _____

(e) Using the results of (c) and (d), calculate the peak-to-peak values of the various currents of the network using Ohm's law.

$I_{T(p-p)} =$ _____ , $I_{R(p-p)} =$ _____ , $I_{C(p-p)} =$ _____

(f) Calculate the rms values of the measured quantities and insert below. Compare to the results of (b).

$I_{T(rms)} =$ _____ , $I_{R(rms)} =$ _____ , $I_{C(rms)} =$ _____

(g) Is the total current I_T larger than each branch current? Should it be?

(h) Using the input voltage as a reference ($\mathbf{E} = E \angle 0°$), and the measured rms values of the currents I_R and I_C, draw a phasor diagram to scale and measure the current I_T. How does it compare to the measured value? From the phasor diagram, determine the angle θ_T between I_T and I_R (same as between E and I_T), the angle θ between I_T and I_C, and the angle θ_1 between I_R and I_C.

I_T (diagram) = _____ , I_T (measured) = _____

$\theta_T =$ _____ , $\theta =$ _____ , $\theta_1 =$ _____

(i) Connect the oscilloscope as shown in Fig. 7.2. Do not reintroduce the resistor R_{S_1}. It will permit a measurement of the phase angle between the two branch currents I_R and I_C. Record the value of θ_1. Points $a, b,$ and c appear in Fig. 7.4.

θ_1 (measured) = _____ , θ_1 [Part 2(h)] = _____

(j) Reintroduce the resistor R_{S_1} and connect the oscilloscope as shown in Fig. 7.3. The phase angle obtained will be between the input voltage E and current I_T or between I_R and I_T since E and I_R are in phase.

θ_T (measured) = _____ , θ_T [Part 2(h)] = _____

(k) Using the fact that $\theta_T + \theta + \theta_1 = 180°$, find the measured value of θ using the measured values of (i) and (j). Compare to the results of (h).

θ (measured) = _____ , θ [Part 2(h)] = _____

Part 3   R-L-C Parallel Network

(a) Construct the network of Fig. 7.5. Insert the measured resistor values. As in the earlier parts, ignore the sensing resistors and R_l, compared to $R, X_L,$ and X_C in your calculations.

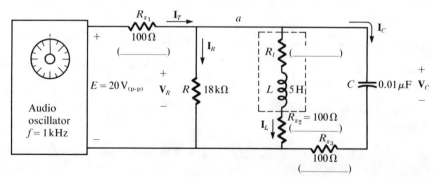

FIG. 7.5

(b) Measure the peak-to-peak values of V_R, $V_{R_{S_2}}$, and $V_{R_{S_3}}$ and determine their rms values.

$V_{R(\text{p-p})} = $ _____ , $V_{R_{S_{2}(\text{p-p})}} = $ _____ , $V_{R_{S_{3}(\text{p-p})}} = $ _____ ,

$V_{R(\text{rms})} = $ _____ , $V_{R_{S_{2}(\text{rms})}} = $ _____ , $V_{R_{S_{3}(\text{rms})}} = $ _____

(c) Reverse the input leads to the oscillator and measure the voltage of $V_{R_{S_1}}$.

$V_{R_{S_{1}(\text{p-p})}} = $ _____ , $V_{R_{S_{1}(\text{rms})}} = $ _____

(d) Verify Kirchhoff's current law at node a. That is, show with a phasor diagram (with $\mathbf{E}$ as the reference $\mathbf{E} = E\ \underline{/0°}$) that the vector sum of $\mathbf{I}_R$, $\mathbf{I}_L$, and $\mathbf{I}_C$ is equal to $\mathbf{I}_T$. The currents can be determined from the measurements of Part 3(b).

(e) Using the nameplate values, calculate the input current I_T and compare to the value obtained in (d).

$I_{T(\text{rms})}$ (measured) = _____ , $I_{T(\text{rms})}$ (calculated) = _____

Series-Parallel Sinusoidal Circuits

Experiment ac

8

OBJECT

To investigate the behavior of series-parallel sinusoidal networks.

EQUIPMENT REQUIRED

Resistors
1—100 Ω, 18 kΩ
2—10 kΩ

Inductors
1—5 H

Capacitors
1—0.01 μF

Instruments
1—DMM
1—Oscilloscope
1—Audio oscillator

EQUIPMENT ISSUED

TABLE 8.1

Item	Manufacturer and Model No.	Laboratory Serial No.
DMM		
Oscilloscope		
Audio Oscillator		

TABLE 8.2

Resistors	
Nominal Value	Measured Value
100 Ω	
18 kΩ	
10 kΩ	
10 kΩ	

RÉSUMÉ OF THEORY

In the previous experiments, we showed that Kirchhoff's voltage and current laws hold for ac series and parallel circuits. In fact, all of the previously used rules, laws, and methods of analysis apply equally well for both dc and ac networks. The major difference for ac circuits is that one now uses reactance, resistance, and impedance instead of solely resistance.

Consider the common series-parallel circuit of Fig. 8.1.

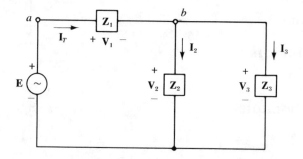

FIG. 8.1

The various impedances shown could be made up of many elements in a variety of configurations. No matter how varied or numerous the elements might be, $\mathbf{Z}_1$, $\mathbf{Z}_2$, and $\mathbf{Z}_3$ represent the total impedance for that branch. For example, $\mathbf{Z}_1$ might be as shown in Fig. 8.2.

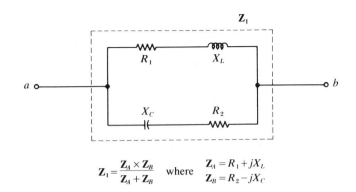

$$\mathbf{Z}_1 = \frac{\mathbf{Z}_A \times \mathbf{Z}_B}{\mathbf{Z}_A + \mathbf{Z}_B} \quad \text{where} \quad \begin{array}{l} \mathbf{Z}_A = R_1 + jX_L \\ \mathbf{Z}_B = R_2 - jX_C \end{array}$$

FIG. 8.2

The currents and voltages in Fig. 8.1 can be found by applying any of the methods outlined for dc networks:

$$\mathbf{Z}_T = \mathbf{Z}_1 + \frac{\mathbf{Z}_2 \mathbf{Z}_3}{\mathbf{Z}_2 + \mathbf{Z}_3}$$

$$\mathbf{I}_1 = \frac{\mathbf{E}}{\mathbf{Z}_T}$$

and

$$\mathbf{I}_2 = \frac{\mathbf{Z}_3 \mathbf{I}_1}{\mathbf{Z}_3 + \mathbf{Z}_2} \qquad \text{(current divider rule)}$$

$\mathbf{I}_3$ can be determined using Kirchhoff's current law:

$$\mathbf{I}_3 = \mathbf{I}_1 - \mathbf{I}_2$$

Ohm's law provides the voltages:

$$\mathbf{V}_1 = \mathbf{I}_1 \mathbf{Z}_1, \qquad \mathbf{V}_2 = \mathbf{I}_2 \mathbf{Z}_2, \qquad \mathbf{V}_3 = \mathbf{I}_3 \mathbf{Z}_3$$

Keep in mind that the voltages and currents are phasor quantities that have both magnitude and an associated angle.

The power factor $\cos \theta = R_T / Z_T$ where R_T is the equivalent total resistance of the circuit at the input terminals.

PROCEDURE

Part 1   R-L Series-Parallel Network

(a) Construct the network of Fig. 8.3. Insert the measured values for each resistor. R_S is the sensing resistor for the current $\mathbf{I}_L$. At the applied frequency, the resistors R_S and R_l can be ignored in comparison with the other elements of the network.

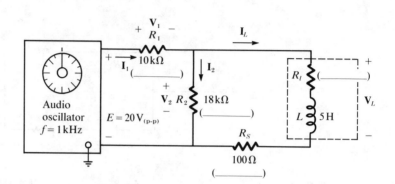

FIG. 8.3

(b) Set the input voltage to $20\,\mathrm{V_{(p-p)}}$ with the oscilloscope, and measure the voltages V_2 and V_{R_S}.

$$V_{2(\mathrm{p\text{-}p})} = \underline{\hspace{3cm}}, \quad V_{R_{S(\mathrm{p\text{-}p})}} = \underline{\hspace{3cm}}$$

Determine the rms value of each and insert in Table 8.3.

TABLE 8.3

Quantity	Computed (Theoretical)	Measured
$E_{(\mathrm{rms})}$		
$V_{1(\mathrm{rms})}$		
$V_{2(\mathrm{rms})}$		
$V_{L(\mathrm{rms})}$		
$I_{1(\mathrm{rms})}$		
$I_{2(\mathrm{rms})}$		
$I_{L(\mathrm{rms})}$		
$|Z_T|$		
θ_T, F_p		
$V_1 \angle \theta_1$		
$V_2 \angle \theta_2$		
$V_L \angle \theta_L$		

(c) Calculate $I_{L(\mathrm{rms})}$ and insert in Table 8.3.

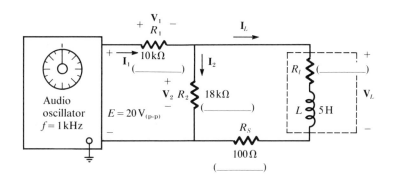

FIG. 8.3

(b) Set the input voltage to $20\,V_{(p-p)}$ with the oscilloscope, and measure the voltages V_2 and V_{R_S}.

$$V_{2(p-p)} = \underline{\hspace{3cm}}, \quad V_{R_{S(p-p)}} = \underline{\hspace{3cm}}$$

Determine the rms value of each and insert in Table 8.3.

TABLE 8.3

Quantity	Computed (Theoretical)	Measured
$E_{(rms)}$		
$V_{1(rms)}$		
$V_{2(rms)}$		
$V_{L(rms)}$		
$I_{1(rms)}$		
$I_{2(rms)}$		
$I_{L(rms)}$		
$|Z_T|$		
θ_T, F_p		
$V_1 \angle \theta_1$		
$V_2 \angle \theta_2$		
$V_L \angle \theta_L$		

(c) Calculate $I_{L(rms)}$ and insert in Table 8.3.

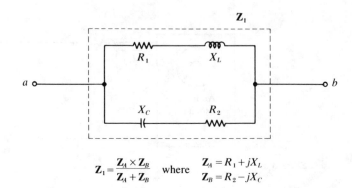

FIG. 8.2

$$\mathbf{Z}_1 = \frac{\mathbf{Z}_A \times \mathbf{Z}_B}{\mathbf{Z}_A + \mathbf{Z}_B} \quad \text{where} \quad \begin{array}{l} \mathbf{Z}_A = R_1 + jX_L \\ \mathbf{Z}_B = R_2 - jX_C \end{array}$$

The currents and voltages in Fig. 8.1 can be found by applying any of the methods outlined for dc networks:

$$\mathbf{Z}_T = \mathbf{Z}_1 + \frac{\mathbf{Z}_2 \mathbf{Z}_3}{\mathbf{Z}_2 + \mathbf{Z}_3}$$

$$\mathbf{I}_1 = \frac{\mathbf{E}}{\mathbf{Z}_T}$$

and

$$\mathbf{I}_2 = \frac{\mathbf{Z}_3 \mathbf{I}_1}{\mathbf{Z}_3 + \mathbf{Z}_2} \quad \text{(current divider rule)}$$

$\mathbf{I}_3$ can be determined using Kirchhoff's current law:

$$\mathbf{I}_3 = \mathbf{I}_1 - \mathbf{I}_2$$

Ohm's law provides the voltages:

$$\mathbf{V}_1 = \mathbf{I}_1 \mathbf{Z}_1, \qquad \mathbf{V}_2 = \mathbf{I}_2 \mathbf{Z}_2, \qquad \mathbf{V}_3 = \mathbf{I}_3 \mathbf{Z}_3$$

Keep in mind that the voltages and currents are phasor quantities that have both magnitude and an associated angle.

The power factor $\cos \theta = R_T / Z_T$ where R_T is the equivalent total resistance of the circuit at the input terminals.

PROCEDURE

Part 1   R-L Series-Parallel Network

(a) Construct the network of Fig. 8.3. Insert the measured values for each resistor. R_S is the sensing resistor for the current $\mathbf{I}_L$. At the applied frequency, the resistors R_S and R_l can be ignored in comparison with the other elements of the network.

(d) Remove R_S and measure the voltage V_L.

$V_{L(\text{p-p})} =$ _____

Calculate the rms value and insert in Table 8.3.

(e) Reverse the input leads to the oscillator and measure the voltage V_1 (a common ground for the oscilloscope and oscillator is then a possibility).

$V_{1(\text{p-p})} =$ _____

Calculate the rms value and insert in Table 8.3.

(f) Determine I_1 and I_2 (rms values) from the voltage readings V_1 and V_2 and include in Table 8.3.

(g) From the above readings, determine the magnitude of $\mathbf{Z}_T$ and include it in Table 8.3.

(h) Connect the oscilloscope as shown in Fig. 8.4 and measure the phase angle θ_T between the input voltage $\mathbf{E}$ and the input current $\mathbf{I}_1$. Include the results in Table 8.3.

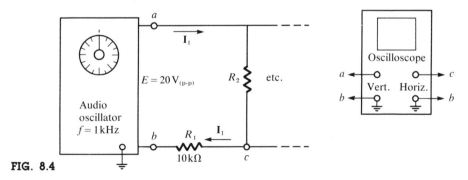

FIG. 8.4

(i) Calculate the power factor $F_p = \cos \theta_T$ and insert in Table 8.3.

(j) Determine $V_1 \angle \theta_1$ using Ohm's law and assuming that $\mathbf{E} = E \angle 0°$. Include in Table 8.3.

(k) Using $\mathbf{E} = E \angle 0°$ as a reference vector, sketch a phasor diagram of $\mathbf{E}$ and $\mathbf{V}_1$. Determine $\mathbf{V}_2$ from the diagram using Kirchhoff's voltage law:

$$\mathbf{E} = \mathbf{V}_1 + \mathbf{V}_2$$

Include the result in the "Measured" column of Table 8.3.

(l) Determine $\mathbf{V}_L = V_L \angle \theta_L$ and insert in Table 8.3.

(m) Using the measured resistor values and the nameplate values of the coil, calculate all of the quantities appearing in Table 8.3 and include them in the table. Compare your results to the measured values. Again, ignore the effects of the sensing resistors and R_l.

Part 2   R-C Series-Parallel Network

(a) Construct the network of Fig. 8.5. Insert the measured resistor values.

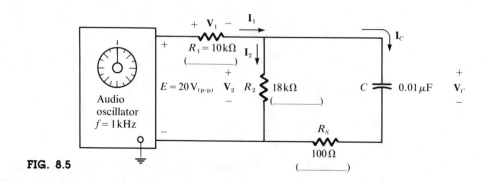

FIG. 8.5

(b) In this part of the experiment, the steps required to determine the quantities appearing in Table 8.4 are not defined in detail. The measurement steps and calculations are left to you to perform on an independent basis. As in Part 1, ignore R_S in comparison to the other elements of the network at the applied frequency.

TABLE 8.4

Quantity	Computed (Theoretical)	Measured
$E_{(rms)}$		
$V_{1(rms)}$		
$V_{2(rms)}$		
$V_{R_S(rms)}$		
$V_{C(rms)}$		
$I_{1(rms)}$		
$I_{2(rms)}$		
$I_{C(rms)}$		
$|Z_T|$		
θ_T, F_p		
$V_1 \angle \theta_1$		
$V_2 \angle \theta_2$		
$V_C \angle \theta_C$		

(c) How do the calculated and measured values compare?

Part 3 R-L-C Series-Parallel Network

(a) Construct the network of Fig. 8.6. Insert the measured resistor values. Ignore the effects of R_S and R_l compared to the other elements of the network at the applied frequency.

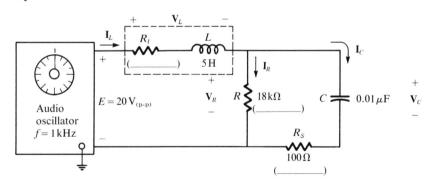

FIG. 8.6

(b) Complete Table 8.5.

TABLE 8.5

Quantity	Computed (Theoretical)	Measured
$E_{(rms)}$		
$V_{L(rms)}$		
$V_{R(rms)}$		
$V_{C(rms)}$		
$I_{L(rms)}$		
$I_{R(rms)}$		
$I_{C(rms)}$		
$|Z_T|$		
θ_T, F_p		
$V_L \; \angle \theta_L$		
$V_R \; \angle \theta_R$		
$V_C \; \angle \theta_C$		

(c) How do the calculated and measured values compare?

OBJECT

To study Thevenin's theorem and the theorem of maximum power transfer as it applies to ac circuits and sources.

EQUIPMENT REQUIRED

Resistors

1—1 kΩ, 18 kΩ

2—10 kΩ

1—(0–10 kΩ) potentiometer

Capacitors

1—0.47 μF

2—1 μF

Inductors

1—5 H

Instruments

1—DMM

1—Oscilloscope

1—Audio oscillator

Thevenin's Theorem and Maximum Power Transfer

Experiment ac

9

EQUIPMENT ISSUED

TABLE 9.1

Item	Manufacturer and Serial No.	Laboratory Serial No.
DMM		
Oscilloscope		
Audio Oscillator		

TABLE 9.2

Resistors	
Nominal Value	Measured Value
1 kΩ	
10 kΩ	
10 kΩ	
18 kΩ	

RÉSUMÉ OF THEORY

Thevenin's theorem states that any two-terminal, linear ac network can be replaced by an equivalent circuit consisting of a voltage source in series with an impedance. To apply this theorem, follow these simple steps:

1.   Remove that portion of the network across which the Thevenin equivalent circuit is found.
2.   Short out all voltage sources and open all current sources. (This is never done practically, but only theoretically.)
3.   Calculate Z_{Th} across the two terminals in question.
4.   Replace all sources.
5.   Calculate E_{Th}, which is the voltage across the terminals in question.
6.   Draw the Thevenin equivalent circuit and replace that portion of the circuit originally removed.
7.   Solve for the voltage or current originally desired.

Example: Using Thevenin's theorem, find the current through R in Fig. 9.1.

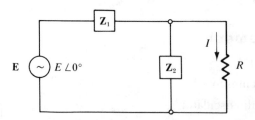

FIG. 9.1

Step 1:   Remove R. See Fig. 9.2(a).
Step 2:   Replace **E** by a short-circuit equivalent. See Fig. 9.2(a).

Step 3: Solve for $\mathbf{Z}_{Th}$. In this case, $\mathbf{Z}_{Th} = \mathbf{Z}_1 || \mathbf{Z}_2$. See Fig. 9.2(a).
Step 4: Replace $\mathbf{E}$. See Fig. 9.2(b).
Step 5: Calculate $\mathbf{E}_{Th}$ from

$$\mathbf{E}_{Th} = \frac{\mathbf{Z}_2}{\mathbf{Z}_1 + \mathbf{Z}_2}\mathbf{E}$$

See Fig. 9.2(b).
Step 6: Draw the equivalent circuit and replace R. See Fig. 9.2(c).
Step 7: Calculate $\mathbf{I}$ from

$$\mathbf{I} = \frac{\mathbf{E}_{Th}}{\mathbf{Z}_{Th} + \mathbf{R}}$$

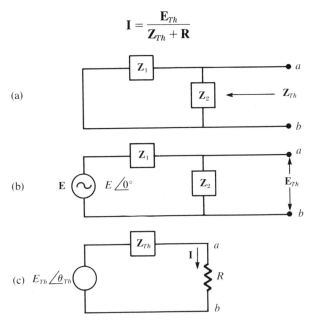

FIG. 9.2

MAXIMUM POWER TRANSFER THEOREM

The maximum power transfer theorem states that for circuits with ac sources, maximum power will be transferred to a load when the load impedance is the conjugate of the Thevenin impedance across its terminals. See Fig. 9.3.

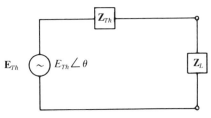

FIG. 9.3

For maximum power transfer, if

$$\mathbf{Z}_{Th} = R \pm jX$$

then

$$\mathbf{Z}_{L} = R \mp jX$$

PROCEDURE

Part 1

(a) Measure the dc resistance of the coil and include it on Fig. 9.4. Indicate the measured values of R, R_1, and R_2 from Table 9.2.

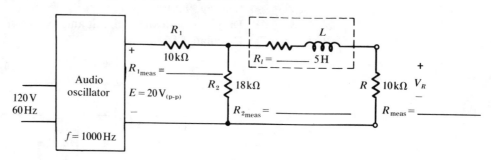

FIG. 9.4

(b) With E set at 20 V$_{(p-p)}$, measure V_R.

$V_{R(p-p)} = $ _____ , $V_{R(rms)} = $ _____

(c) Remove the resistor R and measure the open-circuit voltage across the resulting terminals. This is the magnitude of $\mathbf{E}_{Th}$. As shown in (d), $\mathbf{E}_{Th}$ and $\mathbf{E}$ will have the same phase angle.

$\left| \mathbf{E}_{Th} \right|_{(p-p)} = $ _____ , $\left| \mathbf{E}_{Th} \right|_{(rms)} = $ _____

(d) Using the measured resistance levels, calculate $\mathbf{E}_{Th}$ and its associated angle. Compare to the magnitude of (c). Assume $\mathbf{E} = E \, \underline{/0°}$.

$\mathbf{E}_{Th} = $ _____

(e) Calculate $\mathbf{Z}_{Th}$ (magnitude and angle).

$\mathbf{Z}_{Th} = $ _____

(f) Insert the calculated values obtained for Z_{Th} and E_{Th} in Fig. 9.5. Using the 0–10-kΩ potentiometer and the amplitude control on the audio oscillator, set the values of the Thevenin circuit. Also include any reactive elements needed. Then measure the voltage $V_{R(p\text{-}p)}$ and compare to the measurements of (b).

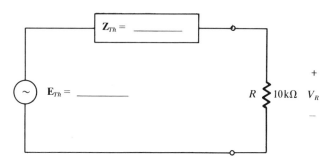

FIG. 9.5

$V_{R(p\text{-}p)} =$ _____ , $V_{R(rms)} =$ _____

(g) Is the Thevenin theorem verified?

(h) From your previous experience, develop a laboratory procedure (in detail) that would allow you to determine both the magnitude and the angle of Z_{Th}.

(i) Test your procedure of (h) and compare to the calculated value.

$|Z_{Th}| =$ _____ , $\theta_{Th} =$ _____

Part 2   Maximum Power Transfer

(a) Construct the circuit of Fig. 9.6. Include the measured resistor values.

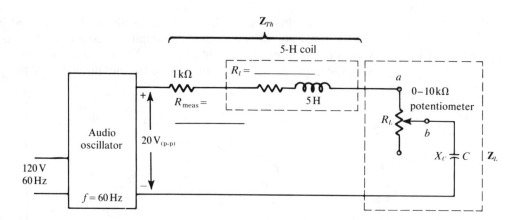

FIG. 9.6

Set the 0–10-kΩ potentiometer to $R_{meas} + R_l$ as required for maximum power transfer. Indicate this value in each row of Table 9.3 in the column labeled "R_T." You are given two 1-μF and one 0.47-μF capacitor. By placing different combinations of these capacitors in parallel, you can achieve the values shown for C in Table 9.3. Insert the fixed value of $\mathbf{Z}_{Th}$ (in rectangular form) in each row of that column and calculate $\mathbf{Z}_L$ (in rectangular form) for each value of C. Record V_{ab} for each value of C, and calculate the power to the load through V_{ab}^2/R_T for each setting of C. Remember, $R_L = R_T$.

TABLE 9.3

$\mathbf{Z}_{Th}$	R_T	C	V_{ab}	$P_{load} = V_{ab}^2/R_T$	$\mathbf{Z}_{load}$
		0.47 μF			
		1.00 μF			
		1.47 μF			
		2.00 μF			
		2.47 μF			

(b) On Graph 9.1, plot $P = V_{ab}^2/R_T$ versus X_C (as found in the $\mathbf{Z}_L$ column).

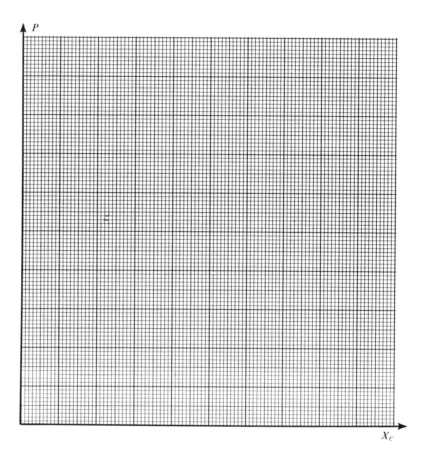

GRAPH 9.1

(c) Is maximum power transferred when $R_L = R_T$ and $X_C = X_L$ as required by the theorem?

OBJECT

To investigate the characteristics of a series resonant circuit.

EQUIPMENT REQUIRED

Resistors

1—10 Ω, 91 Ω

Inductors

1—1 mH, 10 mH

Capacitors

1—0.1 μF, 1 μF

Instruments

1—DMM

1—Oscilloscope

1—Audio oscillator

Series Resonant Circuits

Experiment
ac
10

EQUIPMENT ISSUED

TABLE 10.1

Item	Manufacturer and Model No.	Laboratory Serial No.
DMM		
Oscilloscope		
Audio Oscillator		

TABLE 10.2

Resistors	
Nominal Value	Measured Value
10 Ω	
91 Ω	

RÉSUMÉ OF THEORY

In a series R-L-C circuit, there exists one frequency at which $X_L = X_C$ or $\omega L = 1/\omega C$. At this frequency the circuit is in resonance, and the input voltage and current are in phase. At resonance, the circuit is resistive in nature and has a minimum value of impedance or a maximum value of current.

The resonant radian frequency $\omega_s = 1/\sqrt{LC}$ and frequency $f_s = 1/2\pi\sqrt{LC}$. The Q of the circuit is defined as $\omega_s L/R$ and affects the selectivity of the circuit. High-Q circuits are very selective. At resonance, $V_C = QE_{input}$. The half-power frequencies f_1 and f_2 are defined as those frequencies at which the power dissipated is one-half the power dissipated at resonance. In addition, the current is 0.707 (or $1/\sqrt{2}$) times the current at resonance.

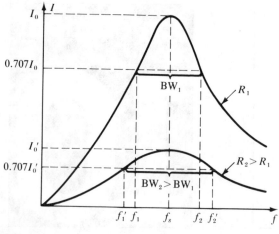

FIG. 10.1

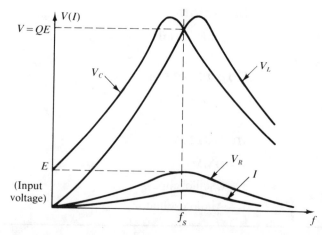

FIG 10.2

The bandwidth $BW = f_2 - f_1$. The smaller the bandwidth, the more selective a circuit. In Fig. 10.1, note that increasing R results in a less selective circuit. Figure 10.2 shows the voltages across the three elements, versus the frequency. The voltage across the resistor, V_R, has exactly the same shape as the current since it differs by the constant R. V_R is a maximum at resonance. V_C and V_L are equal at resonance (f_s) since $X_L = X_C$, but note that they are not maximum at the resonant frequency. At frequencies below f_s, $V_C > V_L$; at frequencies above f_s, $V_L > V_C$, as indicated in Fig. 10.2.

PROCEDURE

Part 1 Low-Q Circuit

(a) Construct the circuit of Fig. 10.3. Insert the measured resistance values.

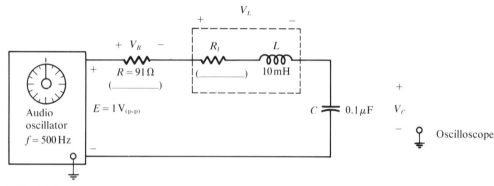

FIG. 10.3

(b) Using the nameplate values and measured resistance values, compute the radian frequency ω_s, the frequency f_s, and the Q_s of the circuit of Fig. 10.3 at resonance. Include the effects of R_l in your calculations.

$$\omega_s = \underline{\hspace{3cm}}, f_s = \underline{\hspace{3cm}}, Q_s = \underline{\hspace{3cm}}$$

(c) Energize the circuit and set the oscillator to the frequencies indicated in Table 10.3. At each frequency, reset the input to $1\,V_{(p-p)}$ and measure the voltages V_C^*, V_R^* and V_L^*. Take a few extra readings near the resonant frequency to improve your data.

---

*In order to establish a common ground for both the oscilloscope and oscillator, the resistor and inductor must occupy the position of the capacitor C when the voltage measurements across these elements are made.

TABLE 10.3

Frequency	$V_{R(p\text{-}p)}$	$V_{L(p\text{-}p)}$	$V_{C(p\text{-}p)}$	$I_{(p\text{-}p)} = V_{R(p\text{-}p)}/R$
500				
1,000				
2,000				
3,000				
4,000				
5,000				
6,000				
7,000				
8,000				
9,000				
10,000				
f_s (calculated)				
Near f_s				

Part 2 Higher-Q Circuit

(a) Repeat Parts 1(a), (b), and (c) using $R = 10\,\Omega$. Record the results in Table 10.4.

$$\omega_s = \underline{\hspace{2cm}}, f_s = \underline{\hspace{2cm}}, Q_s = \underline{\hspace{2cm}}$$

(b) On Graph 10.1, draw the curves of current $I_{(p\text{-}p)}$ (in milliamperes) versus frequency for Parts 1 and 2.

TABLE 10.4

Frequency	$V_{R\text{(p-p)}}$	$V_{L\text{(p-p)}}$	$V_{C\text{(p-p)}}$	$I_{\text{(p-p)}} = V_{R\text{(p-p)}}/R$
500				
1,000				
2,000				
3,000				
4,000				
5,000				
6,000				
7,000				
8,000				
9,000				
10,000				
f_s (calculated)				
Near f_s				

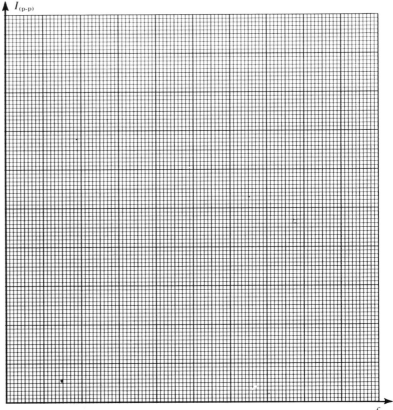

GRAPH 10.1   0

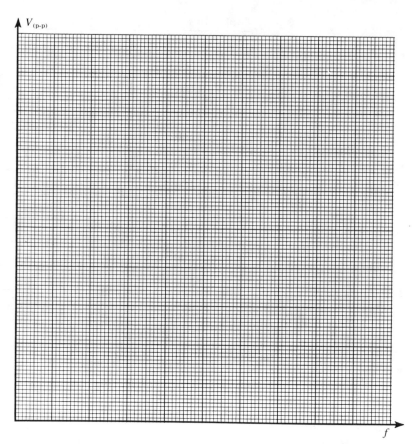

GRAPH 10.2

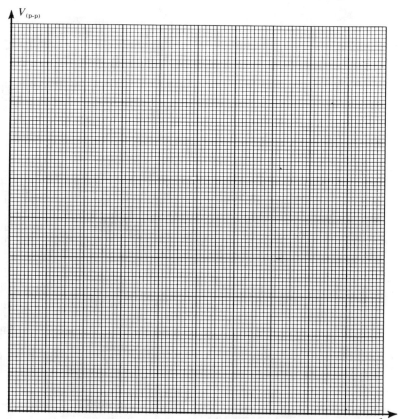

GRAPH 10.3

(c) On Graph 10.2, plot V_R, V_L, and V_C versus frequency for Part 1.

(d) On Graph 10.3, plot V_R, V_L, and V_C versus frequency for Part 2.

(e) How do the curves of Parts 2(b), (c), and (d) compare to those in the Résumé of Theory?

(f) Indicate the resonant and half-power frequencies and the bandwidth on each curve. What is the bandwidth in hertz for each curve using the results of Part 2(b)?

BW $(R = 91\,\Omega) = $ _____ , BW $(R = 10\,\Omega) = $ _____

Which curve is more selective? Why?

(g) Calculate the Q_s for each part from the data *at the resonant frequency*. That is, use the peak-to-peak values of V_C and E and the following equation:

$$Q_s = \frac{V_C}{E}$$

$Q_s\,(R = 91\,\Omega) = $ _____ , $Q_s\,(R = 10\,\Omega) = $ _____

(h) Calculate the Q_s of each circuit from the curves using $Q = f_s/\text{BW}$.

$Q_s\,(R = 91\,\Omega) =$ _____ , $Q_s\,(R = 10\,\Omega) =$ _____

How do the Q_s's from Part 1(b) and (c) compare?

How do the Q_s's obtained in Part 2(g) and (h) compare with the calculated Q_s of Part 2(a)?

Part 3

(a) If the inductor of Fig. 10.3 is changed to 1 mH and the capacitance to $1\,\mu\text{F}$, how will the response curve change?

(b) Make the circuit changes indicated in 3(a) and plot the curve of $I_{(p-p)}$ versus frequency on Graph 10.1. Create your own table below for the data obtained. Does the resulting plot verify the conclusions of 3(a)?

OBJECT

To investigate the characteristics of a parallel resonant circuit.

EQUIPMENT REQUIRED

Resistors

1—10 Ω, 91 Ω, 10 kΩ

Inductors

1—1 mH

Capacitors

1—1 μF

Instruments

1—DMM
1—Oscilloscope
1—Audio oscillator

Parallel Resonant Circuits

Experiment
ac
11

EQUIPMENT ISSUED

TABLE 11.1

Item	Manufacturer and Model No.	Laboratory Serial No.
DMM		
Oscilloscope		
Audio Oscillator		

TABLE 11.2

Resistors	
Nominal Value	**Measured Value**
$10\,\Omega$	
$91\,\Omega$	
$10\,k\Omega$	

RÉSUMÉ OF THEORY

The basic components of a parallel resonant network appear in Fig. 11.1.

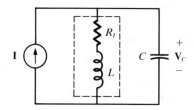

FIG. 11.1

For parallel resonance, the following condition must be satisfied:

$$\frac{1}{X_C} = \frac{X_L}{X_L^2 + R_l^2} \tag{11.1}$$

At resonance, the impedance of the network is resistive and determined by:

$$Z_{T_p} = \frac{L}{R_l C} \tag{11.2}$$

The resonant frequency is determined by:

$$f_p = \frac{1}{2\pi\sqrt{LC}}\sqrt{1 - \frac{R_l^2 C}{L}} \tag{11.3}$$

which reduces to:

$$f_p = \frac{1}{2\pi\sqrt{LC}}$$ (11.4)

when

$$Q_{coil} = \frac{X_L}{R_l} \geq 10$$

For parallel resonance, the curve of interest is that of $\mathbf{V}_C$ versus frequency due to electronic considerations that often place this voltage at the input to the following stage. It has the same shape as the resonance curve for the series configuration with the bandwidth determined by

$$\text{BW} = f_2 - f_1$$ (11.5)

Where f_2 and f_1 are the cut-off or band frequencies.

PROCEDURE

Part 1 High-Q Parallel Resonant Circuit

(a) Construct the network of Fig. 11.2. Insert the measured resistance values.

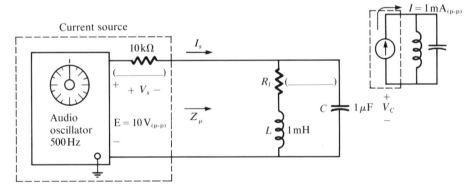

FIG. 11.2

(b) The input voltage E must be maintained at $10\,V_{(p-p)}$. Be sure to reset E after each new frequency is set on the oscillator. Keep in mind that V_s can only be measured with the oscilloscope if the leads to the oscillator are reversed and a common ground is established between the oscilloscope and oscillator.

Since the input to a parallel resonant circuit is usually a constant-current device such as a transistor, the input current I_s has been designed to be fairly constant in magnitude for the frequency range of interest. The input impedance (Z_p) of the parallel resonant circuit will always be sufficiently less than the $10\,k\Omega$ resistor, to permit the following approximation:

$$I_s = \frac{E}{10\,k\Omega + Z_p} \cong \frac{E}{10\,k\Omega} = \frac{10\,V_{(p\text{-}p)}}{10\,k\Omega} = 1\,mA_{(p\text{-}p)}$$

(c) Compute the resonant frequency of the network of Fig. 11.2 using the nameplate data and the measured resistor values.

$f_p = $ _____

(d) Calculate the input impedance at resonance using the following equation:

$$Z_p = R_p = \frac{L}{R_l C}$$

$Z_p = $ _____

(e) Compare the 10-kΩ resistor to the result of (c). Is it reasonable to assume that the input current is fairly constant for the frequency range of interest?

(f) Is this a high- or low-Q circuit? Find Q_p using

$$Q_p = \frac{X_L}{R_l}$$

$Q_p = $ _____

(g) Vary the frequency from 500 to 10 kHz and record the readings in Table 11.3. Maintain $E = 10 \text{ V}_{(p\text{-}p)}$ as indicated in (b). Take a few extra readings around the resonant condition. Use the oscilloscope for all measurements. Calculate $I_{s(p\text{-}p)}$ from the readings for $V_{s(p\text{-}p)}$.

TABLE 11.3

Frequency	$V_{C(p\text{-}p)}$	$V_{s(p\text{-}p)}$	$I_{s(p\text{-}p)}$
500			
1,000			
2,000			
3,000			
4,000			
5,000			
6,000			
7,000			
8,000			
9,000			
10,000			
f_p (calculated)			
Near f_p			

(h) Plot $V_{C(p\text{-}p)}$ versus frequency on Graph 11.1.

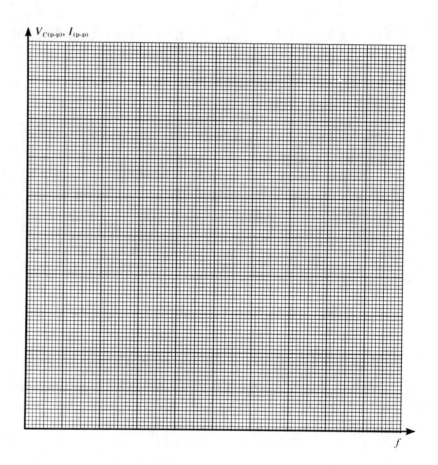

GRAPH 11.1

(i) Calculate $I_{s(p-p)}$ at each frequency and plot the curve on Graph 11.1.

(j) Using the results of (i), determine the BW and cut-off frequencies.

$$BW = \underline{\hspace{2cm}}, f_1 = \underline{\hspace{2cm}}, f_2 = \underline{\hspace{2cm}}$$

(k) Compute the bandwidth from $BW = f_p/Q_p$ and compare to the results of (j).

$$BW \text{ (computed)} = \underline{\hspace{2cm}}, \quad BW \text{ (measured)} = \underline{\hspace{2cm}}$$

Part 2   Lower-Q Parallel Resonant Circuit

(a) Insert the 91 Ω resistor in series with the inductor of Fig. 11.2 so that the total resistance of the inductor branch is $R_l + 91\ \Omega$ (measured value). The effect will be to reduce the Q_p of the network as determined by $Q_p = X_L/R$.

Determine the resonant frequency of the network using Eq. (11.3). The value of R in the equation must now include the 91-Ω resistor.

$$f_p = \underline{\hspace{2cm}}$$

(b) Calculate the input impedance at resonance.

$$Z_{T_p} = \underline{\hspace{2cm}}$$

(c) Calculate the Q_p of the network at the resonant frequency. Compare to the results of Part 1(f).

$Q_p =$ _____

(d) Repeat Part 1(g) and insert the data in a table that you can create in the space provided below. Take a few extra readings around the resonant frequency.

(e) Plot the results on Graph 11.1 and compare results.

(f) Determine the BW and cut-off frequencies from the plot of Part 2(e).

BW = _____ , $f_2 =$ _____ , $f_1 =$ _____

(c) Calculate the Q_p of the network at the resonant frequency. Compare to the results of Part 1(f).

$Q_p =$ _____

(d) Repeat Part 1(g) and insert the data in a table that you can create in the space provided below. Take a few extra readings around the resonant frequency.

(e) Plot the results on Graph 11.1 and compare results.

(f) Determine the BW and cut-off frequencies from the plot of Part 2(e).

BW = _____ , $f_2 =$ _____ , $f_1 =$ _____

(**j**) Using the results of (i), determine the BW and cut-off frequencies.

BW = _____ , f_1 = _____ , f_2 = _____

(**k**) Compute the bandwidth from BW = f_p/Q_p and compare to the results of (j).

BW (computed) = _____ , BW (measured) = _____

Part 2 Lower-Q Parallel Resonant Circuit

(**a**) Insert the 91 Ω resistor in series with the inductor of Fig. 11.2 so that the total resistance of the inductor branch is $R_l + 91\ \Omega$ (measured value). The effect will be to reduce the Q_p of the network as determined by $Q_p = X_L/R$.

Determine the resonant frequency of the network using Eq. (11.3). The value of R in the equation must now include the 91-Ω resistor.

f_p = _____

(**b**) Calculate the input impedance at resonance.

Z_{T_p} = _____

OBJECT

To study the characteristics of a transformer.

EQUIPMENT REQUIRED

Resistors

1—100 Ω, 220 Ω, 10 kΩ

Capacitors

1—15 µF.

Transformers

Filament, 120-V, primary; 12.6-V, secondary

Instruments

1—DMM

1—Oscilloscope

1—Audio Oscillator

The Transformer

Experiment
ac
12

EQUIPMENT ISSUED

TABLE 12.1

Item	Manufacturer and Model No.	Laboratory Serial No.
DMM		
Oscilloscope		
Audio Oscillator		

TABLE 12.2

Resistors	
Nominal Value	Measured Value
100 Ω	
220 Ω	
10 kΩ	

RÉSUMÉ OF THEORY

A *transformer* is a device that transfers energy from one circuit to another by electro-magnetic induction. The energy is always transferred without a change in frequency. The winding connected to the energy source is called the *primary,* while the winding connected to the load is called the *secondary.* A step-up transformer receives electrical energy at one voltage and delivers it at a higher voltage. Conversely, a step-down trans-former receives energy at one voltage and delivers it at a lower voltage. Transformers require little care and maintenance because of their simple, rugged, and durable con-struction. The efficiency of power transformers is also quite high.

The operation of the transformer is based on the principle that electrical energy can be transferred efficiently by mutual induction from one winding to another.

The physical construction of a transformer is shown in Fig. 12.1.

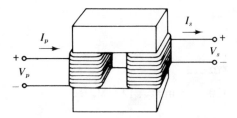

FIG. 12.1

For practical applications, the apparent power at the input to the primary circuit ($P_a = V_p I_p$) is equal to the apparent power rating at the secondary ($P_a = V_s I_s$). That is,

$$V_p I_p = V_s I_s$$

(12.1)

It can also be shown that the ratio of the primary voltage V_p to the secondary voltage V_s is equal to the ratio of the number of turns of the primary to the number of turns of the secondary:

$$\boxed{\frac{V_p}{V_s} = \frac{N_p}{N_s}} \qquad \text{(12.2)}$$

The currents in the primary and secondary circuits are related in the following manner:

$$\boxed{\frac{I_p}{I_s} = \frac{N_s}{N_p}} \qquad \text{(12.3)}$$

The impedance of the secondary circuit is electrically reflected to the primary circuit as indicated by the following expression:

$$\boxed{Z_p = a^2 Z_s} \qquad \text{where } a = \frac{N_p}{N_s} \qquad \text{(12.4)}$$

PROCEDURE

Part 1   Phase Relationship Between the Transformer Primary and Secondary Voltages

Set up the circuit of Fig. 12.2.

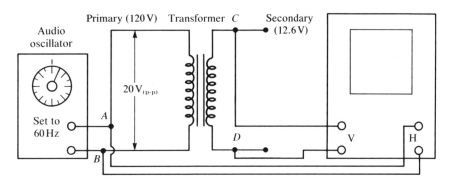

FIG. 12.2

Set the horizontal mode control of the oscilloscope to external. Adjust the horizontal deflection sensitivity so that both horizontal and vertical deflections are equal. What does the pattern on the screen indicate as to the phase relationship of the two voltages? Give reasons for your answer.

Part 2   Voltage, Current, and Turns Ratio of the Transformer

(a) Construct the circuit of Fig. 12.3. Insert the measured resistor values.

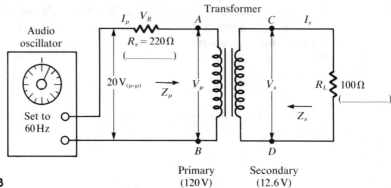

FIG. 12.3

Measure and record the primary and secondary rms voltage with the DMM.

$V_p =$ _____ , $V_s =$ _____

Using the measured values above and Eq. (12.2), calculate the turns ratio N_p/N_s.

$a = N_p/N_s =$ _____

(b) Determine the current I_s shown in Fig. 12.3 using Ohm's law ($I_s = V_s/R_L$). Using Eq. (12.3), calculate I_p.

I_s (measured) = _____ , I_p (calculated) = _____

(c) Determine the current I_p shown in Fig. 12.3 using Ohm's law ($I_p = V_R/R$).

$I_p =$ _____

How does this measured value compare to the calculated value of (b)? Is this a step-up or step-down transformer? Explain.

(d) Set up the network of Fig. 12.4. Note the new position of terminals A through D. In essence, the transformer is hooked up in the reverse manner. Insert the measured resistor values.

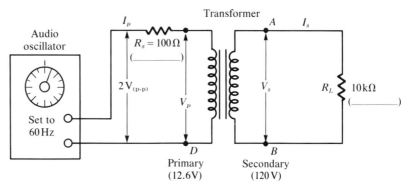

FIG. 12.4

Now measure V_p, V_s, and I_s. Use the technique of the previous parts to determine I_p and I_s.

$V_p =$ _____ , $I_p =$ _____

$V_s =$ _____ , $I_s =$ _____

Using Eqs. (12.2) and (12.3), calculate the turns ratio. Is the transformer being used as before? Explain.

N_p/N_s [Eq. (12.2)] = _____ , N_p/N_s [Eq. (12.3)] = _____

Part 3   Power Dissipation

Using the measured values of I_p, V_p, I_s, and V_s, calculate the apparent power ($P = VI$) of the primary and secondary circuits of the transformer of Fig. 12.3.

P (primary) = _____ , P (secondary) = _____

What conclusion can you draw from your calculations?

Part 4 Impedance Transformation

Reconnect the transformer as shown in Fig. 12.3.

(a) Using Eq. (12.4), calculate the reflected impedance (Z_p) for the network of Fig. 12.3. Do not include R in Z_p.

Z_p (calculated) = _____

(b) Calculate Z_p from the data of Parts 2(a) and (c).

Z_p = _____

How does this value of Z_p compare to the calculated value in (a)?

(c) Using Eq. (12.4), calculate the reflected impedance Z_s. The transformation ratio a remains the same.

(d) Calculate Z_s from the data of Parts 2(a) and (b).

Z_s (calculated) = _____

Calculate the ratio Z_p/Z_s. What does this number represent?

Z_p/Z_s = _____

(e) Disconnect the circuit (Fig. 12.3) from the audio oscillator. Connect the 15-μF capacitor in series with the 100-Ω resistor. Calculate the magnitude of the reflected impedance Z_p for this circuit.

$Z_p =$ _____

(f) Connect the circuit to the audio oscillator. Measure I_p and V_p.

$I_p =$ _____ , $V_p =$ _____

Calculate Z_p using the values of I_p and V_p above.

$Z_p =$ _____

How does this value of Z_p compare to the value calculated in (e)?

Currents and Voltages in Balanced Three-Phase Systems

Experiment ac

13

OBJECT

To investigate the current and voltage relations in three-phase systems with balanced Y and Δ loads.

EQUIPMENT REQUIRED

Resistors

3—100 Ω, 330 Ω, 10 kΩ, 18 kΩ, 33 kΩ

Instruments

1—DMM

1—Phase sequence indicator

Power Supply

Three-phase, 120/208 V, 60 Hz

EQUIPMENT ISSUED

TABLE 13.1

Item	Manufacturer and Model No.	Laboratory Serial No.
DMM		
Phase Sequence Indicator		

TABLE 13.2

Resistors			
Nominal Value	Measured Value	Nominal Value	Measured Value
100 Ω		10 kΩ	
100 Ω		18 kΩ	
100 Ω		18 kΩ	
330 Ω		18 kΩ	
330 Ω		33 kΩ	
330 Ω		33 kΩ	
10 kΩ		33 kΩ	
10 kΩ			

RÉSUMÉ OF THEORY

In a balanced three-phase system, the three-phase voltages are equal in magnitude and 120° out-of-phase. The same holds true for the line voltages, phase currents, and line currents. The system is balanced if the impedance of each phase is the same. For the balanced Y load, the line current is equal to the phase current, and the line voltage is the square root of 3 (or 1.73) times the phase voltage. For the balanced Δ load, the line and phase voltages are equal, but the line current is the square root of 3 (or 1.73) times the phase current. The relationship used to convert a balanced Δ load to a balanced Y load is

$$\mathbf{Z}_Y = \frac{\mathbf{Z}_\Delta}{3} \tag{13.1}$$

Since the sum (phasor) of three equal quantities 120° out-of-phase is zero, if a neutral wire is connected to a balanced, three-phase, Y-connected load, the current in this neutral wire will be zero. If the loads are unbalanced, the current will not be zero.

The phase sequence of voltage does not affect the magnitude of currents in a balanced system. However, if the load is unbalanced, changing the phase sequence will change the magnitude of the currents. The sequence of voltages determines the direction of rotation of a three-phase motor.

PROCEDURE

Note: Be absolutely sure that the power is turned off when making changes in the network configuration or inserting and removing instruments.

Part 1   Phase-Sequence Indicator

Connect the sequence indicator to the power source as shown in Fig. 13.1. Turn the power on. If the 1-2-3 light is brighter than the 3-2-1 light, then the phase sequence is 1-2-3 or $E_{12}(E_{AB})$, $E_{23}(E_{BC})$, and $E_{31}(E_{CA})$, which means that if E_{12} is the reference, then E_{23} lags E_{12} by 120°, and E_{31} lags E_{23} by 120°. If the 3-2-1 lamp is brighter, then the sequence is 3-2-1. Record the phase sequence of the line voltages.

Sequence = _____

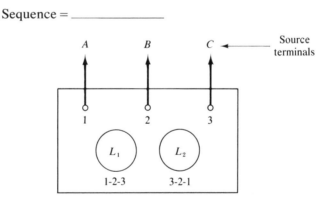

FIG. 13.1

Read the magnitude of the line voltages (E_{AB}, E_{BC}, and E_{CA}) and the phase voltages (E_{AN}, E_{BN}, and E_{CN}) using the DMM.

$E_{AB} =$ _____ , $E_{BC} =$ _____ , $E_{CA} =$ _____
$E_{AN} =$ _____ , $E_{BN} =$ _____ , $E_{CN} =$ _____

Draw the phasor diagram of the line voltages showing magnitude and phase angle if E_{AB} is the reference voltage at an angle of 0°.

Part 2   Resistors in a Balanced Δ

Construct the network of Fig. 13.2.

(a) Measure the three-phase voltages and line voltages.

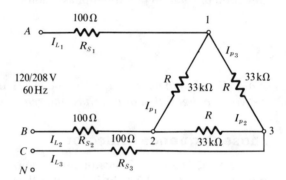

FIG. 13.2

$V_{AB} =$ _____ , $V_{BC} =$ _____ , $V_{CA} =$ _____

$V_{12} =$ _____ , $V_{23} =$ _____ , $V_{31} =$ _____

What is the relationship between the line voltage and the phase voltage in a balanced Δ load?

(b) Measure the voltage across the sensing resistors with the DMM.

$V_{R_{S_1}} =$ _____ , $V_{R_{S_2}} =$ _____ , $V_{R_{S_3}} =$ _____

Calculate the line currents using the sensing voltages and Ohm's law.

$I_{R_{S_1}} = I_{L_1} =$ _____ , $I_{R_{S_2}} = I_{L_2} =$ _____ ,

$I_{R_{S_3}} = I_{L_3} =$ _____

(c) Using Ohm's law, determine the phase currents.

$I_{P_1} =$ _____ , $I_{P_2} =$ _____ , $I_{P_3} =$ _____

(d) For a balanced Δ load, how are the line currents related (in magnitude)?

(e) For a balanced Δ load, how are the phase currents related (in magnitude)?

(f) For a balanced Δ load, how are the line and phase currents related (in magnitude)?

Part 3   Resistor in a Balanced Y

Construct the network of Fig. 13.3.

(a) Measure the three-phase voltages and line voltages.

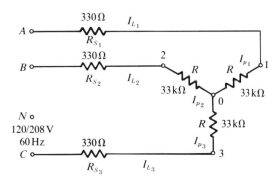

FIG. 13.3

$V_{AB} =$ _____ , $V_{BC} =$ _____ , $V_{CA} =$ _____
$V_{01} =$ _____ , $V_{02} =$ _____ , $V_{03} =$ _____

What is the relationship between the magnitudes of the line voltages and the phase voltages of a balanced Y-connected load?

(b) Measure the voltage across the sensing resistors with the DMM.

$V_{R_{S_1}} =$ _____ , $V_{R_{S_2}} =$ _____ , $V_{R_{S_3}} =$ _____

Calculate the line currents using the sensing voltages and Ohm's law.

$I_{R_{S_1}} = I_{L_1} =$ _____ , $I_{R_{S_2}} = I_{L_2} =$ _____ ,
$I_{R_{S_3}} = I_{L_3} =$ _____

(c) Using Ohm's law, determine the phase currents.

$I_{P_1} =$ _____ , $I_{P_2} =$ _____ , $I_{P_3} =$ _____

(d) For a balanced Y-connected load, how are the line currents related (in magnitude)?

(e) For a balanced Y-connected load, how are the phase currents related (in magnitude)?

(f) For a balanced Y-connected load, how are the line and phase currents related?

Part 4   Resistors in a Combination Y-Δ Configuration

(a) Construct the network of Fig. 13.4.

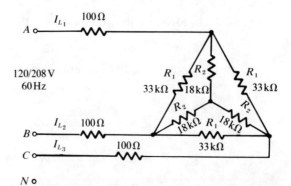

FIG. 13.4

(b) Read the line voltages V_{AB}, V_{BC}, and V_{CA}, and determine the line currents from the voltage across the sensing resistors.

$V_{AB} =$ _____ , $V_{BC} =$ _____ , $V_{CA} =$ _____

$I_{L_1} =$ _____ , $I_{L_2} =$ _____ , $I_{L_3} =$ _____

(c) Using the measured line voltage (average value) and nameplate component values, calculate a line current (magnitude) using a Y-Δ conversion, and compare it to a measured value from (b). Ignore the effects of the 100-Ω sensing resistors in your calculations.

I_L (measured) = _____ , I_L (calculated) = _____

(d) Repeat (c), but now convert the balanced Δ to a balanced Y.

I_L (calculated) = _____

Power Measurements in Three-Phase Systems

Experiment ac 14

OBJECT

To investigate the two-wattmeter method of measuring power in three-phase systems.

EQUIPMENT REQUIRED

Resistors:

3—250 Ω (225 W), wire-wound

Instruments

1—DMM
2—1000 W maximum wattmeters (HPF)

Power Supply

Three-phase, 120/208 V, 60 Hz

EQUIPMENT ISSUED

TABLE 14.1

Item	Manufacturer and Model No.	Laboratory Serial No.
DMM		
Wattmeter		
Wattmeter		

TABLE 14.2

Resistors	
Nominal Value	Measured Value
250 Ω	
250 Ω	
250 Ω	

RÉSUMÉ OF THEORY

The total average power to a three-phase load circuit is given by Eqs. (14.1) and (14.2):

$$P_T = 3E_p I_p \cos\theta \qquad \text{(14.1)}$$

where E_p = phase voltage, I_p = phase current, $\cos\theta$ = power factor, and θ = phase angle between E_p and I_p.

$$P_T = \sqrt{3} E_L I_L \cos\theta \qquad \text{(14.2)}$$

where E_L = line voltage, I_L = line current, $\cos\theta$ = power factor, and θ = phase angle between E_p and I_p.

The power to a three-phase load circuit can be measured in two ways:

1. Three-wattmeter method
2. Two-wattmeter method

THREE-WATTMETER METHOD

The connections for the wattmeters for a Δ and a Y circuit are shown in Fig. 14.1. The total power P_T is equal to the sum of the wattmeter readings.

Note that in each case, connections must be made to the individual load in each phase, which is sometimes awkward, if not impossible. A more feasible and economical method is the two-wattmeter method.

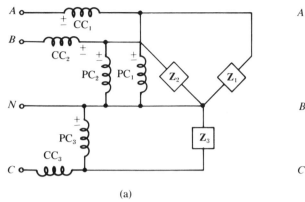

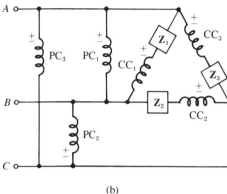

(a)   (b)

FIG. 14.1

TWO-WATTMETER METHOD

With the two-wattmeter method, it is not necessary to be concerned with the accessibility of the load. The two wattmeters are connected as shown in Fig. 14.2.

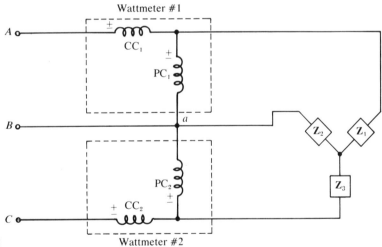

FIG. 14.2

It can be shown that the two-wattmeter method of measuring total average power yields the correct value under any conditions of load.

If we plot a curve of power factor versus the ratio of the wattmeter readings P_1/P_2 where P_1 is always the smaller reading, we obtain the curve appearing in Fig. 14.3.

The graph shows that if the power factor is equal to 1 (resistive circuit), then $P_1 = P_2$ and the readings are additive. If the power factor is zero (reactive), then $P_1 = P_2$; but P_1 is negative, so $P_T = 0$. At a 0.5 power factor, one wattmeter reads zero, and the other reads the total power. It is indicative from the graph that if $F_P > 0.5$, the readings are to be added; and if $F_p < 0.5$, the readings are to be subtracted.

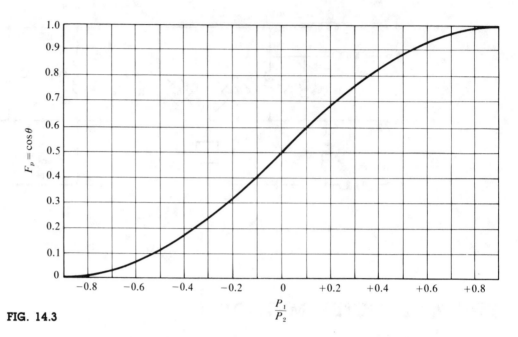

FIG. 14.3

The two-wattmeter method will read the total power in a three-wire system even if the system is unbalanced. For three-phase, four-wire systems (balanced or unbalanced), three wattmeters are needed.

It can be shown that the power read by each wattmeter is given by the following relationships:

$$P_2 = E_L I_L \cos(\theta - 30°) \qquad \text{(14.3)}$$

$$P_1 = E_L I_L \cos(\theta + 30°) \qquad \text{(14.4)}$$

$$P_T = P_2 \pm P_1 \qquad \begin{array}{l}\text{(the algebraic sum of } P_1 \text{ and } P_2, \\ \text{where } P_1 \text{ is the smaller reading)}\end{array} \qquad \text{(14.5)}$$

Another advantage of the two-wattmeter method is that it allows us to calculate the phase angle (θ) and therefore the power factor (F_p) using the expressions

$$\tan \theta = \sqrt{3}\, \frac{P_2 - P_1}{P_2 + P_1} \qquad \text{(14.6)}$$

$$F_p = \cos \theta \qquad \text{(14.7)}$$

PROCEDURE FOR CONNECTING THE WATTMETER USING THE TWO-WATTMETER METHOD

Connect the potential coils (PC) in the circuit last, and use the insulated alligator clip leads for their connections to line B. (See Fig. 14.2.) Close the breaker. If either watt-meter reads down-scale, shut down and reverse the current coil (CC) of the wattmeter that reads down-scale. Apply power again and read both wattmeters.

To find the sign of the lower-reading wattmeter, proceed as follows. If watt-meter #1 is the lower reading, unclip lead a of the PC coil and touch to any point on line A. If the wattmeter deflects up-scale, the reading is to be added (+). If the deflection is down-scale, the reading is negative and is to be subtracted (−). If wattmeter #2 is the lower-reading wattmeter, then the PC lead a is touched to line C for the test.

PROCEDURE

Part 1   Balanced Δ-Connected Resistor Loads

(a) Measure the resistance of three resistors. Insert in Fig. 14.4.

$R_1 =$ _____ , $R_2 -$ _____ , $R_3 =$ _____ _____

(b) Construct the network of Fig. 14.4. Refer to the procedure for connecting the wattmeter. *Exercise caution at all times!* If in doubt, ask your instructor.

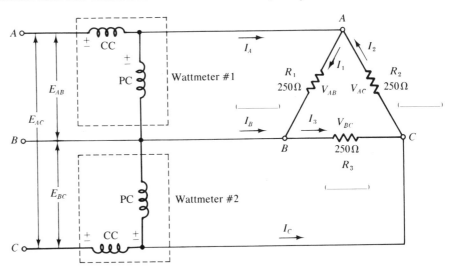

FIG. 14.4

Measure E_{AB}, E_{BC}, and E_{AC}.

$E_{AB} =$ _____ , $E_{BC} =$ _____ , $E_{AC} =$ _____

Are these the line or phase voltages of the supply? Explain.

Are these the same as the phase voltages of the load V_{AB}, V_{BC}, and V_{AC}? Explain.

(c) Calculate the magnitude of the currents I_1, I_2, and I_3.

$I_1 = $ _____ , $I_2 = $ _____ , $I_3 = $ _____

Are these the line or phase currents? Explain.

Calculate the values of the currents I_A, I_B, and I_C.

$I_A = $ _____ , $I_B = $ _____ , $I_C = $ _____

Are these the line or phase currents? Explain.

What is the relationship between (I_A, I_B, and I_C) and (I_1, I_2, and I_3)?

(d) Calculate the power dissipated by each resistor.

$P_1 = $ _____ , $P_2 = $ _____ , $P_3 = $ _____

What is the total power?

$P_T = $ _____

Read the wattmeters.

$P_1 =$ _____ , $P_2 =$ _____

What is the total power?

$P_T =$ _____

How does this value compare to the one calculated above?

Calculate the phase angle and the power factor of the circuit.

$\theta =$ _____ , $F_p =$ _____

Compute P_1/P_2. Does this agree with the graph of Fig. 14.3? Explain.

$P_1/P_2 =$ _____

If three wattmeters were to be used, what would be the reading of each watt-meter?

$P_1 =$ _____ , $P_2 =$ _____ , $P_3 =$ _____

Part 2   Balanced Four-Wire Y-Connected Resistor Load

(a) Construct the circuit of Fig. 14.5. Refer to the procedure for connecting the wattmeter. *Exercise caution at all times!* If in doubt, ask your instructor. Insert the measured value of each resistor.

Measure the voltages V_{AN}, V_{BN}, and V_{CN}.

$V_{AN} =$ _____ , $V_{BN} =$ _____ , $V_{CN} =$ _____

Are these the line or phase voltages? Explain.

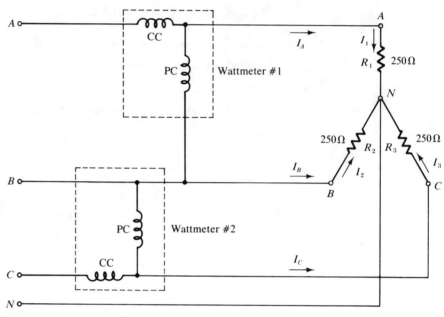

FIG. 14.5

Measure the voltages E_{AB}, E_{BC}, and E_{AC}.

$E_{AB} =$ _____ , $E_{BC} =$ _____ , $E_{AC} =$ _____

What is the relationship between (V_{AN}, V_{BN}, and V_{CN}) and (E_{AB}, E_{BC}, and E_{AC})?

Calculate E_{AB}/V_{AN}, E_{BC}/V_{BN}, and E_{AC}/V_{CN}.

Do these ratios confirm the theory? Explain.

(b) Calculate the magnitude of the currents I_1, I_2, and I_3.

$I_1 = $ _____ , $I_2 = $ _____ , $I_3 = $ _____

Are these the line or phase currents? Explain.

How are these currents related to the magnitude of I_A, I_B, and I_C?

Calculate the magnitude of I_A, I_B, and I_C.

$I_A = $ _____ , $I_B = $ _____ , $I_C = $ _____

(c) Calculate the power delivered to the circuit.

$P_T = $ _____

Read the wattmeters.

$P_1 = $ _____ , $P_2 = $ _____

Calculate P_T from P_1 and P_2.

$P_T = $ _____

(d) Calculate the power factor F_p and the phase angle θ.

$F_p =$ _____ , $\theta =$ _____

Calculate P_1/P_2.

$P_1/P_2 =$ _____

Do the values of θ, F_p, and P_1/P_2 agree with the graph of Fig. 14.3?

(e) What effect would there be if the neutral wire were removed? Explain.

(f) Sketch the connections if three wattmeters were used to measure the total power to the network of Fig. 14.5.

Parts List for the Experiments

dc (REQUIRED)

Resistors

1/2-W carbon
    1 of any value
1-W carbon
    1 of any value
2-W carbon
    1—10 Ω, 47 Ω, 91 Ω, 100 Ω, 470 Ω, 1 MΩ
    2—220 Ω, 1.2 kΩ, 2.2 kΩ, 3.3 kΩ, 10 kΩ
    3—330 Ω, 1 kΩ, 100 kΩ
    1—unknown between 47 Ω and 220 Ω
Variable
    1—(0–1 kΩ) potentiometer, linear, carbon
    1—(0–10 kΩ) potentiometer, linear, carbon
    1—(0–250 kΩ) potentiometer, linear, carbon

Capacitors

2—100 μF electrolytics

Inductors

1—5 H

Miscellaneous

1—single-pole, single-throw switch
1—1 mA, 1000 Ω meter movement

Instruments

1—VOM
1—DMM
1—dc Power supply, 0–30 V, 0–500 mA (minimum)

dc (OPTIONAL)

Second dc power supply
Commercial Wheatstone bridge

ac (REQUIRED)

Resistors

2-W carbon
  1—$10\,\Omega$, $91\,\Omega$, $220\,\Omega$, $1\,k\Omega$, $1.2\,k\Omega$, $3.3\,k\Omega$, $6.8\,k\Omega$
  3—$100\,\Omega$, $330\,\Omega$, $10\,k\Omega$, $18\,k\Omega$, $33\,k\Omega$
Variable
  1—$(0$–$10\,k\Omega)$ potentiometer, linear, carbon

Capacitors

1—$0.01\,\mu F$, $0.47\,\mu F$, $0.5\,\mu F$, $15\,\mu F$
2—$0.1\,\mu F$, $1\,\mu F$

Inductors

1—$1\,mH$, $10\,mH$
2—$5\,H$

Miscellaneous

1—Single-pole, double-throw switch
1—Transformer, 120 V primary, 12.6 V secondary
2—D batteries and holders

Instruments

1—DMM
1—Audio oscillator
1—General-purpose oscilloscope

Power sources

Three-phase 208 V/120 V supply (for Experiments 13 and 14 only)

ac (OPTIONAL)

1—Phase sequence indicator
3—$250\,\Omega$, 225-W wirewound resistors for Experiment 14 only
2—1000-W, HPF, wattmeters for Experiment 14 only

dc (OPTIONAL)

Second dc power supply
Commercial Wheatstone bridge

ac (REQUIRED)

Resistors

2-W carbon
   1—10 Ω, 91 Ω, 220 Ω, 1 kΩ, 1.2 kΩ, 3.3 kΩ, 6.8 kΩ
   3—100 Ω, 330 Ω, 10 kΩ, 18 kΩ, 33 kΩ
Variable
   1—(0–10 kΩ) potentiometer, linear, carbon

Capacitors

1—0.01 μF, 0.47 μF, 0.5 μF, 15 μF
2—0.1 μF, 1 μF

Inductors

1—1 mH, 10 mH
2—5 H

Miscellaneous

1—Single-pole, double-throw switch
1—Transformer, 120 V primary, 12.6 V secondary
2—D batteries and holders

Instruments

1—DMM
1—Audio oscillator
1—General-purpose oscilloscope

Power sources

Three-phase 208 V/120 V supply (for Experiments 13 and 14 only)

ac (OPTIONAL)

1—Phase sequence indicator
3—250 Ω, 225-W wirewound resistors for Experiment 14 only
2—1000-W, HPF, wattmeters for Experiment 14 only

Parts List
for the Experiments

dc (REQUIRED)

Resistors

1/2-W carbon
   1 of any value
1-W carbon
   1 of any value
2-W carbon
   1—10 Ω, 47 Ω, 91 Ω, 100 Ω, 470 Ω, 1 MΩ
   2—220 Ω, 1.2 kΩ, 2.2 kΩ, 3.3 kΩ, 10 kΩ
   3—330 Ω, 1 kΩ, 100 kΩ
   1—unknown between 47 Ω and 220 Ω
Variable
   1—(0–1 kΩ) potentiometer, linear, carbon
   1—(0–10 kΩ) potentiometer, linear, carbon
   1—(0–250 kΩ) potentiometer, linear, carbon

Capacitors

2—100 μF electrolytics

Inductors

1—5 H

Miscellaneous

1—single-pole, single-throw switch
1—1 mA, 1000 Ω meter movement

Instruments

1—VOM
1—DMM
1—dc Power supply, 0–30 V, 0–500 mA (minimum)

dc AND ac (TOTAL REQUIREMENTS)

Resistors

1/2-W carbon
　　1 of any value
1-W carbon
　　1 of any value
2-W carbon
　　1—10 Ω, 47 Ω, 91 Ω, 470 Ω, 6.8 kΩ, 1 MΩ
　　2—220 Ω, 1.2 kΩ, 2.2 kΩ, 3.3 kΩ
　　3—100 Ω, 330 Ω, 1 kΩ, 10 kΩ, 18 kΩ, 33 kΩ, 100 kΩ
1—unknown between 47 Ω and 220 Ω

Capacitors

1—0.01 μF, 0.47 μF, 0.5 μF, 15 μF
2—0.1 μF, 1 μF
2—100 μF electrolytics

Inductors

1—1 mH, 10 mH
2—5 H

Miscellaneous

1—Single-pole, single-throw switch
1—Single-pole, double-throw switch
1—1 mA, 1000 Ω meter movement
1—Transformer, 120 V primary, 12.6 V secondary
2—D batteries and holders

Instruments

1—VOM
1—DMM
1—dc Power supply, 0–30 V, 0–500 mA (minimum)
1—Audio oscillator
1—General-purpose oscilloscope

Power Sources

Three-phase 208 V/120 V supply (for Experiments ac 13 and ac 14 only)

dc AND ac (OPTIONAL)

Second dc power supply
Commercial Wheatstone bridge
1—Phase sequence indicator
3—250 Ω, 225-W wirewound resistors for Experiment ac 14 only
2—1000-W, HPF, wattmeters for experiment ac 14 only

Appendix

I

Resistor Color Coding

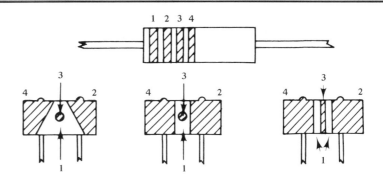

1 First significant digit
2 Second significant digit
3 Multiplying value
4 Tolerance (percent)

FIG. I.1

TABLE I.1   RETMA color code for resistors

Color	1 First Significant Digit	2 Second Significant Digit	3 Multiplier	4 Percent Tolerance
Silver			0.01	10
Gold			0.1	5
Black		0	1.0	
Brown	1	1	10	1
Red	2	2	100	2
Orange	3	3	1,000	3
Yellow	4	4	10,000	4
Green	5	5	100,000	
Blue	6	6	1,000,000	
Purple	7	7	10,000,000	
Gray	8	8	100,000,000	
White	9	9	1,000,000,000	
No color				20

EXAMPLE I.1   Application of resistor color code

Nominal Value	Percent Tolerance	Band				Tolerance	Range
		1	2	3	4		
22,000 Ω	±20	Red	Red	Orange	No Band	±4400 Ω	17,600–26,400 Ω
100 Ω	±5	Brown	Black	Brown	Gold	±5 Ω	95–105 Ω
10 Ω	±10	Brown	Black	Black	Silver	±1 Ω	9–11 Ω
1.2 kΩ	±5	Brown	Red	Red	Gold	±60 Ω	1140–1260 Ω
6.8 MΩ	±20	Blue	Gray	Green	No Band	±1.36 MΩ	5.44–8.16 MΩ

Appendix II

Capacitor Color Coding

MOLDED MICA CAPACITORS

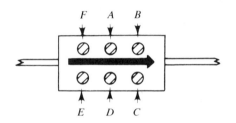

A First significant digit
B Second significant digit
C Multiplying value
D Tolerance (percent)
E Characteristic
F For Mil-C-5 A color code, dot is always black. For EIA color code, dot is always white.

FIG. II.1

TABLE II.1   Color code for molded mica capacitors

Color	A First Significant Digit	B Second Significant Digit	C Multiplier	D Percent Tolerance
Black	0	0	1	20
Brown	1	1	10	1
Red	2	2	100	2
Orange	3	3	1,000	3
Yellow	4	4	10,000	4
Green	5	5	100,000	5
Blue	6	6	1,000,000	6
Violet	7	7	10,000,000	7
Gray	8	8	100,000,000	8
White	9	9	1,000,000,000	9
Gold			0.1	5
Silver			0.01	10

MOLDED CERAMIC CAPACITORS

G A B C D

A   First significant digit
B   Second significant digit
C   Multiplying value
D   Tolerance
G   Temperature coefficient

FIG. II.2

TABLE II.2   Color code for molded ceramic capacitors

Color	A First Significant Digit	B Second Significant Digit	C Multiplier	D Tolerance		G Temperature Coefficient (parts per million per °C)
				Value Greater Than 10 pF (%)	Value 10 pF or Less (pF)	
Black	0	0	1	20	2.0	0
Brown	1	1	10	1		−30
Red	1	1	100	2		−80
Orange	3	3	1,000			−150
Yellow	4	4	10,000			−220
Green	5	5	100,000	5	0.5	−330
Blue	6	6	1,000,000			−470
Violet	7	7	10,000,000			−750
Gray	8	8	0.01		0.25	+30
White	9	9	0.1	10	1.0	+550

Appendix III

Resistance Measurements (VOM)

Never make resistance measurements on a live circuit!

Select the two leads used for resistance measurements. (Consult the instruction manual.) Set the function selector switch to the ohms position. Select the proper range with the range switch. The ranges are usually marked as multiples of R. For example,

$$R \times 1 \qquad R \times 10 \qquad R \times 100 \qquad R \times 1\,\text{k}\,\Omega$$

The value of the resistor can be found by multiplying the reading by the range setting. For example, a reading of 11 on the $R \times 1\,\text{k}\,\Omega$ range is $11 \times 1\,\text{k}\,\Omega = 11\,\text{k}\,\Omega$, or $11{,}000\,\Omega$. Note that the ohms scale (usually the topmost scale) reads from right to left, opposite to the other scales on the meter face.

Before you attach the unknown resistance to the test leads, short the leads together and observe the reading. If the meter does not read zero ohms, adjust the ZERO ADJUST control until it does. Disconnect the leads. The meter should now read infinite resistance (the extreme left-hand index of the scale). If the meter does not read infinite ohms, an adjustment will be required. On the VTVM, this adjustment is made with the OHMS ADJUST control. On the VOM, the control is a mechanical adjustment which requires the use of a screwdriver. Do not attempt this adjustment on the VOM without first consulting your instructor. The zero and infinite ohm adjustments must be checked each time the range of the ohmmeter is changed. Otherwise the readings will be incorrect.

Appendix IV

Proper Use of the VOM Multimeter

1. Always start with the highest range of the instrument and switch down to the proper range successively.
2. Use the range in which the deflection falls in the upper half of the meter scale.
3. Whenever possible, choose a voltmeter range such that the total voltmeter resistance (ohms/volt × FSD) is at least 100 times the resistance of the circuit under test. This rule will prevent erroneous readings due to the loading of the circuit under test.
4. Use an ohmmeter range so that the deflection falls in the uncrowded portion of the scale.
5. Exercise extreme caution when measuring voltages and currents in high-voltage circuits. A safe procedure is to shut down the power, connect the meter, turn the power on, read the meter, and again shut down to disconnect.
6. Try to ascertain the polarity of dc voltages before making the measurement.
7. Never measure resistances in a live circuit. Always shut down before making resistance measurements.
8. Whenever measuring the resistance of a resistor in a circuit, note whether there are any other resistive elements that could cause an error in the reading. It may be necessary to disconnect one side of the resistor before measuring.
9. Check the zero and ohms adjustments each time the range is changed. For proper procedure, see Appendix III.
10. When making measurements, grip the test prods by the handles as close to the lead end as possible. *Do not allow the fingers to touch the prod tips while measuring.*
11. When the instrument is not being used, do not leave it in the ohmmeter function. If the instrument has an OFF position, use it; otherwise, switch to its highest dc voltage range.
13. *Keep the instruments away from the edge of the workbench, and away from heat and dangerous fumes.*

Scientific Notation and Trigonometric Identities

Scientific Notation

The positive exponent of 10 is equal to one less than the number of places to the left of the decimal point:	The negative exponent of 10 is equal to the number of places to the right of the decimal point:

$$10^0 = 1.0$$
$$10^1 = 10.0$$
$$10^2 = 100.0$$
$$10^3 = 1000.0$$
$$10^4 = 10000.0$$
$$10^5 = 100000.0$$

etc.

$$10^0 = 1.0$$
$$10^{-1} = 0.1$$
$$10^{-2} = 0.01$$
$$10^{-3} = 0.001$$
$$10^{-4} = 0.0001$$
$$10^{-5} = 0.00001$$

etc.

Dimensional Prefixes

Prefix	Multiplier
tera	10^{12}
giga	10^{9}
mega	10^{6}
kilo	10^{3}
hecto	10^{2}
deka	10^{1}
deci	10^{-1}
centi	10^{-2}
milli	10^{-3}
micro	10^{-6}
nano	10^{-9}
pico	10^{-12}

Trigonometric Identities

$$\sin(-\theta) = -\sin\theta$$
$$\cos(-\theta) = \cos\theta$$
$$\tan(-\theta) = -\tan\theta$$
$$\sin(\theta + 90°) = \cos\theta$$
$$\cos(\theta - 90°) = \sin\theta$$
$$\sin^2\theta + \cos^2\theta = 1$$
$$\cos(A + B) = \cos A \cos B - \sin A \sin B$$
$$\cos(A - B) = \cos A \cos B + \sin A \sin B$$
$$\sin(A + B) = \sin A \cos B + \cos A \sin B$$
$$\sin(A - B) = \sin A \cos B - \cos A \sin B$$